Teacher's Annotated Edition

HOUGHTON MIFFLIN
math CENTRAL

Daily Cumulative Review

Level 6

HOUGHTON MIFFLIN

Boston • Atlanta • Dallas • Geneva, Illinois • Princeton, New Jersey • Palo Alto

To the Teacher

The Daily Cumulative Review booklet provides a set of
review exercises and word problems for every teaching
lesson in Houghton Mifflin *Math Central*, with an
emphasis on computation. They can be used for
homework or as part of the math class.

1998 Impression
Copyright © 1994 by Houghton Mifflin Company. All rights reserved.

Printed in U.S.A.

ISBN: 0-395-86262-0

23456789-B-03 02 01 00 99 98 97

Name _____

 1 **DAILY CUMULATIVE REVIEW**

Write the answer.

1.	81	2.	70	3.	75
	+ 12		− 40		+ 24
	93		30		99

4.	66	5.	51	6.	96
	− 15		+ 54		− 52
	51		105		44

Compare. Write < or >.

7. 343 $>$ 195   8. 542 $<$ 544   9. 379 $<$ 380

10. 209 $<$ 290   11. 395 $>$ 387   12. 679 $<$ 706

13. 101 $<$ 109   14. 270 $>$ 207   15. 1587 $>$ 1578

16. 4524 $<$ 5422   17. 8070 $>$ 7008   18. 3623 $<$ 3632

19. 2103 $>$ 1320   20. 456 $<$ 465   21. 9841 $>$ 4981

Solve.

22. Toby earned 6 extra-credit points one week and 2
extra-credit points the next week. How many extra-
credit points did he earn during those 2 weeks?

8 extra-credit points

2 ⏵ DAILY CUMULATIVE REVIEW

Write the answer.

1. 33
    + 14

    47

2. 89
    + 20

    109

3. 63
    + 21

    84

4. 58
    − 16

    42

5. 79
    − 19

    60

6. 65
    − 44

    21

Write the numbers in order from least to greatest.

7. 179, 176, 172, 170 _____ 170, 172, 176, 179

8. 348, 834, 483, 384 _____ 348, 384, 483, 834

9. 1930, 1390, 1139, 1319 _____ 1139, 1319, 1390, 1930

10. 1597, 975, 1975, 1759 _____ 975, 1597, 1759, 1975

11. 2843, 3842, 2483, 3428 _____ 2483, 2843, 3428, 3842

Solve.

12. Mrs. Eaton is a bird-watcher. Last year
    she identified 30 birds. This year she
    has identified 22 birds. How many more
    birds must she identify to equal the
    number she identified last year?   _____ 8 birds

Name _____

 3   **DAILY CUMULATIVE REVIEW**

Write the answer.

1. $\begin{array}{r} 201 \\ +\ 74 \\ \hline 275 \end{array}$

2. $\begin{array}{r} 98 \\ -\ 73 \\ \hline 25 \end{array}$

3. $\begin{array}{r} 35 \\ -\ 13 \\ \hline 22 \end{array}$

4. $\begin{array}{r} 242 \\ -\ 150 \\ \hline 92 \end{array}$

5. $\begin{array}{r} 38 \\ +\ 61 \\ \hline 99 \end{array}$

6. $\begin{array}{r} 543 \\ +\ 55 \\ \hline 598 \end{array}$

Write the number in standard form.

7. two hundred

     200
_____

8. one hundred twelve

     112
_____

9. five thousand

     5000
_____

10. 15 thousand

     15,000
_____

11. three thousand twenty

     3020
_____

12. ten thousand one

     10,001
_____

Solve.

13. Ken is reading a book with 207 pages.
Debbie is reading a book with
163 pages. How many more pages is
Ken's book than Debbie's?

     44 pages
_____

Name _____

4 DAILY CUMULATIVE REVIEW

Write the answer.

1. $\begin{array}{r} 108 \\ + 101 \\ \hline 209 \end{array}$

2. $\begin{array}{r} 762 \\ - 310 \\ \hline 452 \end{array}$

3. $\begin{array}{r} 151 \\ + 138 \\ \hline 289 \end{array}$

4. $\begin{array}{r} 967 \\ - 802 \\ \hline 165 \end{array}$

5. $\begin{array}{r} 780 \\ + 116 \\ \hline 896 \end{array}$

6. $\begin{array}{r} 524 \\ - 302 \\ \hline 222 \end{array}$

Round each number to the tens place.

7. 31 ___30___

8. 79 ___80___

9. 674 ___670___

10. 95 ___100___

11. 648 ___650___

12. 492 ___490___

13. 796 ___800___

14. 304 ___300___

Solve.

15. Over the summer, Becky saved $192. For her birthday she received a gift of $25 from her aunt. How much money does she have in all?   ___$217___

16. Esperanza earned $204 in August. She spent $127 on school clothes. How much of her earnings does she have left?   ___$77___

5 ▶ DAILY CUMULATIVE REVIEW

Write the answer.

1.	742	2.	253	3.	496
	− 602		+ 140		− 376
	140		393		120

4.	760	5.	852	6.	320
	+ 128		− 321		+ 277
	888		531		597

Write the value of the underlined digit in short word form.

7. 6348 _____ 3 hundred _____

8. 10,583 _____ 8 tens _____

9. 72,437 _____ 2 thousand _____

10. 908,317 _____ 9 hundred thousand _____

11. 924, 306 _____ 20 thousand _____

Solve.

12. Albert harvested 125 pounds of tomatoes from his garden. He gave away 36 pounds of tomatoes to his neighbors. How many pounds did he have left? _____ 89 pounds _____

Name _____

Write the answer. Use mental math.

1. 99 + 62   _161_   2. $5.00 − $1.99   _$3.01_

3. 310 + 195   _505_   4. 891 − 98   _793_

5. $5.99 + $5.99   _$11.98_   6. 1760 − 295   _1465_

Write each number in standard form.

7. 17 million   _17,000,000_

8. 380 thousand   _380,000_

9. 8 million, 3 thousand, 6   _8,003,006_

10. 5 billion, 19 million, 13   _5,019,000,013_

Solve.

11. Rita sold note paper to help raise
money for the school sports program.
She hoped to sell at least $50 worth
of note paper. Her sales totaled $64.
Did she meet her goal?   _yes_

12. Guy sold magazine subscriptions to
help raise money. He sold $275 worth
of subscriptions. How much more
money did he collect than did Rita?   _$211 more_

Name _____

Answers may vary. Ranges are given.

Estimate. Use the method of your choice.

1.   210
     + 347
    500–550

2.   974
     − 810
    150–200

3.   175
     + 95
    275–300

4.   296
      182
     + 524
    800–1000

5.   850
     − 130
    720–800

6.   1856
     − 470
    1300–1400

Round to the hundreds place.

7. 571   **600**

8. 980   **1000**

9. 1875   **1900**

10. 7503   **7500**

11. 35,138   **35,100**

12. 63,972   **64,000**

Solve.

13. On their vacation, the Alvarez family drove 273 miles one day and 284 miles the next day. How many miles did they travel in all?   **557 miles**

14. On their vacation, the Sternberg family plans to drive 503 miles to a campground. They drive 246 miles on the first day. How many miles do they still need to drive?   **257 miles**

Name _____

Write the answer.

1.	2.	3.
55 + 20 **75**	92 + 91 **183**	204 − 99 **105**

4.	5.	6.
413 − 53 **360**	326 + 98 **424**	983 − 157 **826**

Round to the thousands place.

7. 875 _____**1000**_____   8. 2444 _____**2000**_____

9. 3261 _____**3000**_____   10. $5903 _____**$6000**_____

11. 45,302 _____**45,000**_____   12. 79,837 _____**80,000**_____

13. 4839 _____**5000**_____   14. 17,523 _____**18,000**_____

Solve.

15. In 1989 the salary of the governor of Michigan was
$100,000. In the same year the salary of the governor
of Iowa was $72,500. Which governor received the
greater salary? How much greater was it?

_____**The governor of Michigan; $27,500 more than the**_____

_____**governor of Iowa**_____

Name _____

Write the answer.

1.	88	2.	46	3.	107
	− 56		+ 41		− 81
	32		87		26

4.	92	5.	655	6.	803
	+ 63		− 257		+ 616
	155		398		1419

Write the value of the underlined digit in short word form.

7. 6<u>7</u>,688   _____7 thousand_____

8. 9<u>3</u>09   _____3 hundred_____

9. 8,0<u>6</u>2,700   _____60 thousand_____

10. <u>1</u>69,870   _____1 hundred thousand_____

11. <u>3</u>9,993   _____30 thousand_____

12. 4<u>8</u>,036   _____8 thousand_____

Solve.

13. The average life span of a baboon is 20 years. The average life span of a giraffe is 10 years. How much longer does a baboon usually live than does a giraffe?

_____10 years_____

Name _____

Answers may vary. Ranges are given.

Estimate. Use the method of your choice.

1.   449
   – 75
   300–350

2.   3690
   – 702
   2800–3000

3.   7487
   – 2887
   4000–5000

4.   638
     145
   + 82
   870–900

5.   476
      38
   + 872
   1370–1400

6.   4311
      200
   + 935
   5000–5500

Round each number to the underlined place.

7. 3<u>6</u>5 _____**370**_____

8. <u>1</u>509 _____**2000**_____

9. 1<u>6</u>,900 _____**17,000**_____

10. 2<u>9</u>2,580 _____**290,000**_____

11. 983,4<u>7</u>8 _____**983,480**_____

12. 983,<u>4</u>78 _____**983,500**_____

Solve.

13. A sea wasp jellyfish has tentacles up to 30 feet long. A Portuguese man-of-war jellyfish has tentacles up to 70 feet long. Which sea animal can grow longer tentacles? How much longer?

_____**Portuguese man-of-war; 40 feet longer**_____

Name _____

Write the answer.

1. $\begin{array}{r} 58 \\ + 25 \\ \hline 83 \end{array}$

2. $\begin{array}{r} 641 \\ - 75 \\ \hline 566 \end{array}$

3. $\begin{array}{r} 215 \\ + 30 \\ \hline 245 \end{array}$

4. $\begin{array}{r} 839 \\ - 204 \\ \hline 635 \end{array}$

5. $\begin{array}{r} 672 \\ + 95 \\ \hline 767 \end{array}$

6. $\begin{array}{r} 901 \\ - 119 \\ \hline 782 \end{array}$

Write the value of each expression.

7. What is $a + 2$ if $a = 6$? _____8_____

8. What is $5 + f$ if $f = 4$? _____9_____

9. What is $q + 4$ if $q = 12$? _____16_____

10. What is $6 + k$ if $k = 0$? _____6_____

11. What is $n + 2.3$ if $n = 7.8$? _____10.1_____

12. What is $d + 24.65$ if $d = 83.72$? _____108.37_____

Solve.

13. The oldest recorded age for a black bear is 36 years 10 months. For a white-tailed deer the record age is 17 years 6 months. How much longer did the oldest black bear live than did the oldest white-tailed deer?

_____**19 years 4 months**_____

Name _____

DAILY CUMULATIVE REVIEW

Write the answer.

1.
$$\begin{array}{r} 59 \\ -\ 27 \\ \hline 32 \end{array}$$

2.
$$\begin{array}{r} 810 \\ -\ 684 \\ \hline 126 \end{array}$$

3.
$$\begin{array}{r} 348 \\ +\ 469 \\ \hline 817 \end{array}$$

4.
$$\begin{array}{r} 108 \\ -\ 68 \\ \hline 40 \end{array}$$

5.
$$\begin{array}{r} 819 \\ 83 \\ +\ 200 \\ \hline 1102 \end{array}$$

6.
$$\begin{array}{r} 132 \\ 258 \\ +\ 237 \\ \hline 627 \end{array}$$

Write the value of each expression.

7. What is $9 - s$ if $s = 1$? _____8_____

8. What is $r - 5$ if $r = 10$? _____5_____

9. What is $17 - w$ if $w = 6$? _____11_____

10. What is $4 - n$ if $n = 0.7$? _____3.3_____

11. What is $b - 1.5$ if $b = 13$? _____11.5_____

12. What is $75.3 - y$ if $y = 24.8$? _____50.5_____

Solve.   Answers may vary.

13. The elevation in La Paz, Bolivia is 12,001 feet. The elevation in Caracas, Venezuela is 3418 feet. Estimate the difference in elevation.

about 9000 feet

Name _____

Write the answer. Use mental math.

1. 39 + 26   _____65_____   2. 72 + 99   _____171_____

3. 370 – 199   _____171_____   4. 748 + 95   _____843_____

5. $4.60 – $1.95   _____$2.65_____   6. 1847 – 199   _____1648_____

Write the missing numbers.

7.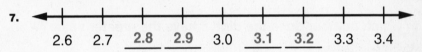

2.6 2.7 **2.8** **2.9** 3.0 **3.1** **3.2** 3.3 3.4

8.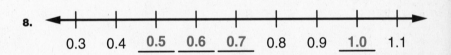

0.3 0.4 **0.5** **0.6** **0.7** 0.8 0.9 **1.0** 1.1

9.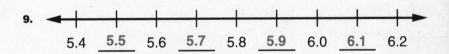

5.4 **5.5** 5.6 **5.7** 5.8 **5.9** 6.0 **6.1** 6.2

Solve.

10. A bagel contains 165 Calories. A one-ounce serving of cream cheese has 100 Calories. How many Calories do they have together?

265 Calories
_____

14 ▸ DAILY CUMULATIVE REVIEW

Write the sum or difference.

1.	4.7 + 0.65 **5.35**	**2.**	84.98 − 3.4 **81.58**	**3.**	3049 + 157 **3206**
4.	0.256 − 0.072 **0.184**	**5.**	7173 + 996 **8169**	**6.**	21,182 − 6,319 **14,863**

In which number does the digit 5 have the greater value?

7. a. 580   **b.** 850   ___**a**___

8. a. 2485   **b.** 2058   ___**b**___

9. a. 35,920   **b.** 30,925   ___**a**___

10. a. 5789   **b.** 12,599   ___**a**___

11. a. 605,878   **b.** 506,787   ___**b**___

12. a. 150,792   **b.** 245,390   ___**a**___

Solve.

13. Mr. Brown paid $82.95 for a bicycle and $19.95 for a safety helmet. Estimate. Did he spend more or less than $100.00?

more than $100.00

Name _____

Answers may vary. Ranges are given.

Estimate the sum or difference.

1.   4.51
      − 3.95
        0.5–1

2.   4.35
      + 6.21
      10–10.5

3. $81.63
      − 15.94
      $60–$65

4.   5.43
       0.4
      + 6.07
      11–12

5.   39.71
     − 21.5
      18–20

6.   2.5 m
      8.8 m
     + 0.9 m
     12 m–13 m

Write each number in standard form.

7. seventeen hundredths   0.17

8. one and twenty-five thousandths   1.025

9. eight and five tenths   8.5

10. two hundred nine thousandths   0.209

11. four hundred and four hundredths   400.04

12. nine thousand six and three tenths   9006.3

Solve.

Answers may vary.

13. At the PTA bake sale, Mrs. Lindeman bought a batch of muffins for $3.50, a loaf of pumpkin bread for $1.77, and dinner rolls for $1.99. Estimate the total cost of her purchases. $7.50

16 DAILY CUMULATIVE REVIEW

Write the sum or difference.

1. $\begin{array}{r} 9.80 \\ + 7.36 \\ \hline 17.16 \end{array}$

2. $\begin{array}{r} 18 \\ - 6.12 \\ \hline 11.88 \end{array}$

3. $\begin{array}{r} 7.02 \\ + 3.39 \\ \hline 10.41 \end{array}$

4. $\begin{array}{r} 13.71 \\ - 8.50 \\ \hline 5.21 \end{array}$

5. $\begin{array}{r} 5.004 \\ + 0.851 \\ \hline 5.855 \end{array}$

6. $\begin{array}{r} 461.52 \\ - 62.76 \\ \hline 398.76 \end{array}$

7. $\begin{array}{r} 48.09 \\ + 37.52 \\ \hline 85.61 \end{array}$

8. $\begin{array}{r} 66.42 \\ + 27.38 \\ \hline 93.80 \end{array}$

9. $\begin{array}{r} 309.03 \\ + 76.87 \\ \hline 385.90 \end{array}$

Name the whole number that each number is closest to.

10. 2.1 ___2___

11. 9.8 ___10___

12. 0.6 ___1___

13. 15.5 ___16___

Solve.

14. During the week before running a marathon, Herman ran these distances on four different days 15 miles, 12 miles, 8 miles, and 15 miles. Use mental math to find the sum of his distances. Explain the method you used.

    ___50 miles; explanation may include: added 15 + 15___

    ___and 12 + 8___

Name _____

 17 **DAILY CUMULATIVE REVIEW** ....

Write the answer. Use mental math.

1. 68 + 39 _____107_____   **2.** 462 − 98 _____364_____

3. $8.29 + $2.99 ___$11.28___   **4.** 144 − 69 _____75_____

5. 604 + 95 _____699_____   **6.** $11.40 − $1.99 ___$9.41___

Write the value of the underlined digit in short word form.

7. 9,618,413
_____9 million_____

8. 48,401
_____4 hundred_____

9. 581,079
_____80 thousand_____

10. 7,357,140,038
_____7 billion_____

11. 625,801,283
___8 hundred thousand___

12. 432,816,550
___4 hundred million___

Solve.

13. Alpine is 90 miles west of El Centro and 25 miles east of San Diego. What is the distance from San Diego to El Centro?   ___115 miles___

Name header with number 18, Daily Cumulative Review
Name _____

18 DAILY CUMULATIVE REVIEW

Answers may vary. Ranges are given.

Estimate. Use the method of your choice.

1.	2.	3.
5854	4615	7763
+ 4905	− 264	− 2314
10,000–11,000	4300–4400	5000–6000

4.	5.	6.
3157	669	1756
388	451	385
+ 1930	+ 834	+ 921
5000–5500	1800–2000	2900–3100

Round to the underlined place.

7. 8<u>9</u>,206

89,000

8. 9,<u>8</u>03,560

9,800,000

9. 5<u>9</u>85

6000

10. <u>4</u>94,205

500,000

Solve.

11. The two towers at the World Trade Center in New York City are 1368 feet tall and 1362 feet tall. If the towers were stacked one on top of the other, how tall would the resulting tower be?

2730 feet

19 DAILY CUMULATIVE REVIEW

Write the sum or difference.

1.	13.686 + 3.084 16.770	2.	8.7 + 5.3 14.0	3.	63.08 − 9.11992 53.96008

4.	7.531 − 1.9 5.631	5.	14.8072 + 11.8641 26.6713	6.	23 − 9.12 13.88

Name the whole number that each decimal is closest to.

7. 8.9 _____9_____   8. 6.68 _____7_____

9. 19.3 _____19_____   10. 1.58 _____2_____

11. 17.88 _____18_____   12. 17.08 _____17_____

13. 25.83 _____26_____   14. 90.07 _____90_____

Solve.

15. To train for a bicycle race, Mark has to ride at least 75 kilometers each week. He keeps a daily log of how far he bicycles. Last week he recorded these distances: 10.9 kilometers, 20.1 kilometers, 35.2 kilometers, and 15.3 kilometers. How much farther than 75 kilometers did he bike last week?

6.5 kilometers more than 75 kilometers

20 DAILY CUMULATIVE REVIEW

Estimate each sum or difference.

Answers may vary. Ranges are given.

1.   4.72 m
      + 3.17 m
      7 m–8 m

2. $12.62
      –   6.10
      $6.00–$6.50

3.   3.051 L
      – 1.562 L
      1.5–2 L

4.   6.30
      8.01
      + 4.20
      18–18.50

5.   4.13
      9.30
      + 7.04
      20–20.5

6. $3.50
      0.28
      + 1.36
      $4.00–$5.00

Round to the nearest hundredth.

7. 7.326   7.33

8. 19.3762   19.38

9. 6.2581   6.26

10. 1.293   1.29

11. 23.706   23.71

12. 49.999   50.00

Solve.

13. There are 3 flavors of frozen yogurt available in the cafeteria, peach, lemon, and strawberry. Students can combine two flavors into a twisted-flavor cone. How many different combinations of two flavors are possible? What are they?

   3 combinations; peach-lemon, peach-strawberry,

   lemon-strawberry

Name _____

21 DAILY CUMULATIVE REVIEW

Write the answer. Use mental math.

1. $27 + 35$ ___62___

2. $73 - 25$ ___48___

3. $63 + 67$ ___130___

4. $88 - 39$ ___49___

5. $460 + 280$ ___740___

6. $530 - 190$ ___340___

Write an equation for the diagram and solve.

7.

equation: ___$n + 7 = 10$___

solution: ___$n = 3$___

8.

equation: ___$15 = n + 5$___

solution: ___$n = 10$___

Solve.

9. $t + 12 = 21$

___$t = 9$___

10. $s - 3 = 13$

___$s = 16$___

Name _____

Write the sum or difference.

1.	9.63	**2.**	8	**3.**	53.115
	− 3.537		− 2.7		− 7.3
	6.093		5.3		45.815

4.	3.47	**5.**	5.1608	**6.**	82.2
	+ 1.87		+ 0.92		+ 90.296
	5.34		6.0808		172.496

Name the tenths decimal that each number is closest to.

7. 2.17 ___2.2___   **8.** 19.882 ___19.9___

9. 0.162 ___0.2___   **10.** 79.51 ___79.5___

11. 390.74 ___390.7___   **12.** 589.96 ___590.0___

Solve.

13. At six weeks old a puppy weighed 2.5 kilograms. One year later the dog weighed 27.3 kilograms. How much weight had the dog gained?

___24.8 kilograms___

14. One pound has 16 ounces. Crystal feeds her dog 12 ounces of food a day. Is 5 pounds of dog food enough to feed her dog for one week?

___no___

Name

Solve. Use mental math when you can.

1. 36 + 47 _____83_____ 2. 71 − 45 _____26_____

3. 245 + 365 _____610_____ 4. 90 − 62 _____28_____

5. 4100 − 1200 _____2900_____ 6. 590 + 640 _____1230_____

Round each number to the underlined place.

7. 6.8<u>3</u>7 _____6.84_____ 8. 52.<u>1</u>65 _____52.2_____

9. 0.2<u>9</u>98 _____0.30_____ 10. 7<u>0</u>9.82 _____710_____

11. 46.<u>0</u>81 _____46.1_____ 12. <u>2</u>0.38 _____20_____

Solve.

13. How many students participated in the survey?

_____510 students_____

14. About how many more students prefer mysteries than biographies?

_____about 40 students_____

Survey of Book Preferences

Favorite Type of Book	Number of Students
Mystery	140
Western	93
Science fiction	121
Biography	101
Other	55

Name _____

Write the sum or difference.

1.	101.7	**2.**	8.831	**3.**	$180.08
	46.92		0.621		54.15
	+ 7.21		+ 9.7		+ 9.77
	155.83		19.152		$244.00

4.	653.3	**5.**	91.23	**6.**	404.69
	− 6.25		− 0.852		− 32.44
	647.05		90.378		372.25

Solve.

7. $a + 15 = 32$

17

8. $41 = b - 29$

70

9. $28 = c - 19$

47

10. $14 = d + 9$

5

11. $65 - d = 34$

31

12. $m - 52 = 78$

130

Solve.

13. Martha has $5.00. She wants to buy eggs, milk, and bread. Eggs cost $1.29 a dozen, milk costs $2.35 a gallon, and whole wheat bread costs $1.79 a loaf. Does she have enough money? If not, how much more money does she need?

No; $0.43 more

25 DAILY CUMULATIVE REVIEW

Write the product.

1. $\begin{array}{r} 20 \\ \times\ 9 \\ \hline 180 \end{array}$

2. $\begin{array}{r} 60 \\ \times\ 20 \\ \hline 1200 \end{array}$

3. $\begin{array}{r} 400 \\ \times\ 30 \\ \hline 12,000 \end{array}$

4. $6 \times 5 \times 4$ _____120_____

5. $7 \times 5 \times 2$ _____70_____

6. $5 \times 5 \times 2 \times 2$ _____100_____

7. $3 \times 2 \times 8 \times 5$ _____240_____

Write each number in word form.

8. 18.01 _____eighteen and one hundredth_____

9. 0.137 _____one hundred thirty-seven thousandths_____

10. 5.009 _____five and nine thousandths_____

11. 43.25 _____forty-three and twenty-five hundredths_____

Read the story. Decide if the underlined sentence makes sense. Explain why or why not.

12. Isabel is making 2 custard pies by doubling the recipe for one pie. The recipe says to bake the pie at 350° for 40 minutes. <u>Isabel thinks, "I will need to bake the 2 pies for 80 minutes."</u>

_____It doesn't make sense. The time required to bake_____

_____the pies together would still be 40 minutes._____

Name _____

26 DAILY CUMULATIVE REVIEW

Write the product.

1. 42
   × 28
   ────
   1176

2. 80
   × 61
   ────
   4880

3. 96
   × 33
   ────
   3168

4. 19
   × 26
   ────
   494

5. 601
   × 59
   ─────
   35,459

6. 75
   × 18
   ────
   1350

Solve for the missing factor. Use mental math.

7. $20 \cdot d = 400$ _____20_____

8. $900 \cdot r = 1800$ _____2_____

9. $s \cdot 4 = 8000$ _____2000_____

10. $35 \cdot t = 3500$ _____100_____

Solve.

11. Mercury's average distance from the sun is 36,000,000 miles. Saturn's average distance from the sun is 900 million miles. How much closer is Mercury to the sun than Saturn?

   864 million miles

12. Jupiter's diameter at its equator is 88,000 miles. Jupiter's polar diameter is 6000 miles shorter. What is the length of Jupiter's polar diameter?

   82,000 miles

Name _____

Write the product. You may use a calculator.

1. 512
    × 432
    221,184

2. 905
    × 157
    142,085

3. 884
    × 227
    200,668

4. 7742
    × 801
    6,201,342

5. 4590
    × 427
    1,959,930

6. 5387
    × 504
    2,715,048

Solve.

7. $6s = 36$ _____ 6 _____

8. $5d = 90$ _____ 18 _____

9. $8t = 72$ _____ 9 _____

10. $250 = 10r$ _____ 25 _____

Write a multiplication expression for each situation.
Tell what the variable stands for.
Accept any reasonable expression.

11. To brush your teeth with the water running uses 2
    gallons of water. The number of gallons of water
    used each day to brush your teeth =

    _____ 2t; t = number of times a day teeth are brushed _____

12. Alice reads the same number of books each month.
    The number of books she reads in a year =

    _____ 12b; b = number of books she reads each month _____

Name _____

Write the answer.

1.
$$4.653$$
$$+ 8.01$$
$$12.663$$

2.
$$89.114$$
$$- 6.135$$
$$82.979$$

3.
$$8856$$
$$\times \quad 9$$
$$79,704$$

4.
$$78$$
$$\times 53$$
$$4134$$

5.
$$29,430$$
$$+ 7,629$$
$$37,059$$

6.
$$0.672$$
$$- 0.4531$$
$$0.2189$$

Estimate. Write < or >.

7. 8 x $7.20 ⊘> $50.00

8. 6 x $2.14 ⊘< $15.00

9. 5 x $0.89 ⊘< $4.50

10. 7 x $9.95 ⊘> $65.00

Write an equation and solve. Accept any reasonable equation.

11. Bags of potatoes weigh 5 pounds. A box of bagged potatoes weighs 40 pounds. How many bags of potatoes are in a box?

$5b = 40$; **8 bags**

12. It costs $3 per car to park in the county park picnic area. How many cars parked there if $57 was collected?

$3c = 57$; **19 cars**

29 DAILY CUMULATIVE REVIEW

Write the answer.

1.
```
  64
- 39
  25
```

2.
```
  400
×   3
 1200
```

3.
```
  81
+ 29
 110
```

4.
```
  1000
×   19
 19,000
```

5.
```
  702
+ 199
  901
```

6.
```
  845
- 298
  547
```

Write the LCM.

7. 4 and 16 ____16____

8. 5 and 9 ____45____

9. 3 and 14 ____42____

10. 4 and 6 ____12____

11. 2, 3, and 4 ____12____

12. 2, 6, and 11 ____66____

Solve.

13. Lee waters her squash plants every third day and her fruit trees once a week. If they are both watered today, in how many days will they again be watered on the same day?

____**21 days**____

14. Mario bought 2 tomato plants for $1.25 each and a six-pack of marigolds for $1.95. How much change did he receive from a five-dollar bill?

____**$0.55**____

Name _____

....

Estimate.　　　　　　　Answers may vary. Ranges are given.

1.　　9.63 kg
　　+ 7.58 kg
　　16 kg–18 kg

2.　　$82.40
　　–　17.35
　　$60.00–$65.00

3.　　83
　　×　2
　　160–170

4.　　490
　　×　71
　　35,000

5.　　7.903
　　– 2.6
　　4.9–5.4

6.　　17,421
　　+ 10,584
　　27,000–28,000

Place the decimal point in the product.

7. 8.3 x 12 → 996 　　　　__99.6__

8. 10 x 0.359 → 359 　　　__3.59__

9. 66 x 14.08 → 92928 　　__929.28__

10. 94 x 8.005 → 75247 　　__752.47__

Read the problem. Then make notes, make a table, or use other strategies to solve.

11. On Monday the balance in Miguel's checking account was $125. During the week he deposited $85 and wrote checks for $12.50 and $16.09. What was the checking account balance at the end of the week?

　　　　　　　　__$181.41__

Name _____

Write the product.

1. 8.2
× 14
114.8

2. 6.07
× 5
30.35

3. 32.71
× 56
1831.76

4. 0.934
× 29
27.086

5. 14.062
× 31
435.922

6. 92.015
× 73
6717.095

Estimate. Write < or >.

7. 3109 + 865 $\bigcirc <$ 4000

8. 1750 − 868 $\bigcirc <$ 900

9. 9.03 − 4.492 $\bigcirc <$ 5

10. 932 + 661 $\bigcirc <$ 1600

Solve.

11. The Torres family budgeted $80 for admission to an amusement park. The cost is $20 for adults and $12.50 for children. Does their budget allow for 2 adult and 3 child admissions?

_____ **yes** _____

12. If only 1 adult goes to the amusement park, how many more children can go to the amusement park with the Torres family?

_____ **1 more child** _____

32 DAILY CUMULATIVE REVIEW

Write the sum or difference.

1.	2.07	2.	9	3.	92.594
	+ 0.58		− 4.78		− 33.96
	2.65		4.22		58.634

4.	2.06	5.	1.45	6.	15.74
	− 0.519		9.63		6.277
	1.541		+ 0.26		+ 10.179
			11.34		32.196

In which number does the digit 4 have the greater value?

7. **a.** 8429   **b.** 8249   _____a_____

8. **a.** 46,067   **b.** 56,804   _____a_____

9. **a.** 6.047   **b.** 6.47   _____b_____

10. **a.** 94,978   **b.** 47,899   _____b_____

Solve.

11. Daryl is building a fence around 3 sides of his garden. The fourth side of the garden is against his house. The garden is a square, 24 feet on a side. How many fence posts does he need if he puts a post every 3 feet?

_____ **25 fence posts** _____

33 DAILY CUMULATIVE REVIEW

Write the answer.

1. $\begin{array}{r} 8075 \\ + 3114 \\ \hline 11,189 \end{array}$	**2.** $\begin{array}{r} \$26.02 \\ - \quad 8.37 \\ \hline \$17.65 \end{array}$	**3.** $\begin{array}{r} 306 \\ \times \quad 92 \\ \hline 28,152 \end{array}$
4. $\begin{array}{r} 190 \\ \times \quad 17 \\ \hline 3230 \end{array}$	**5.** $\begin{array}{r} 23,864 \\ - 13,030 \\ \hline 10,834 \end{array}$	**6.** $\begin{array}{r} 108 \\ 390 \\ + 171 \\ \hline 669 \end{array}$

Write an addition, subtraction, or multiplication expression for each situation. Tell what the variable stands for.

Accept any reasonable expression.

7. The Fernandez family and the Raines family went on a picnic together. There are 6 in the Fernandez family. The number of people on the picnic =

$6 + r$; r = **the number of people in the Raines family**

8. It takes Irene 3 minutes to make a sandwich. The number of minutes she spends making sandwiches =

$3 \cdot s$; s = **the number of sandwiches Irene makes**

9. Sally gave 8 of her books to the library book sale. The number of books she has left =

$b - 8$; b = **the number of books Sally started with**

10. Julio is buying chicken dinners that cost $5 each. The total cost of the dinners =

$n \cdot 5$; n = **the number of dinners bought**

Name _____

Write the answer.

1.
$$\begin{array}{r} 460 \\ \times\ 18 \\ \hline 8280 \end{array}$$

2.
$$\begin{array}{r} 5.398 \\ +\ 0.89 \\ \hline 6.288 \end{array}$$

3.
$$\begin{array}{r} \$4.61 \\ \times\ \ \ \ 4 \\ \hline \$18.44 \end{array}$$

4.
$$\begin{array}{r} 6 \\ -\ 1.53 \\ \hline 4.47 \end{array}$$

5.
$$\begin{array}{r} 9.01 \\ \times\ \ \ 12 \\ \hline 108.12 \end{array}$$

6.
$$\begin{array}{r} 44.7 \\ +\ 8.9 \\ \hline 53.6 \end{array}$$

Name the tenths decimal that each number is closest to.

7. 0.78
   0.8

8. 9.16
   9.2

9. 25.39
   25.4

10. 7.82
   7.8

11. 85.95
   86.0

12. 99.99
   100.0

Read the problem. Then make notes or make a table to solve.

13. Sunshine salads are made with 3 ingredients. The possible ingredients are tomato wedges, cucumber slices, chopped lettuce, alfalfa sprouts, and sunflower seeds. How many different 3-ingredient salads can be made?

10 different salads

35 ▸ DAILY CUMULATIVE REVIEW

Write the product.

1.
$$\begin{array}{r} 144 \\ \times\ 83 \\ \hline 11{,}952 \end{array}$$

2.
$$\begin{array}{r} 6.2 \\ \times\ 68 \\ \hline 421.6 \end{array}$$

3.
$$\begin{array}{r} 56 \\ \times\ 49 \\ \hline 2744 \end{array}$$

4.
$$\begin{array}{r} 7.09 \\ \times\ 20 \\ \hline 141.8 \end{array}$$

5.
$$\begin{array}{r} 479 \\ \times\ 289 \\ \hline 138{,}431 \end{array}$$

6.
$$\begin{array}{r} 9.003 \\ \times\ 650 \\ \hline 5851.95 \end{array}$$

Solve.

7. $y - 8 = 24$ $y = 32$

8. $29 = 6 + t$ $t = 23$

9. $d - 9 = 18$ $d = 27$

10. $42 - k = 37$ $k = 5$

11. $b + 8 = 35$ $b = 27$

12. $21 + h = 64$ $h = 43$

13. $42 = x - 9$ $x = 51$

14. $50 - a = 11$ $a = 39$

Solve.

15. Alicia wants to take horseback riding lessons that cost $15 each. She plans to take 10 lessons, for which she has $85 saved. How much more money does she need?

$65

Name _____

Write the product.

1.	2.	3.
2.32	20	8.5
× 13	× 9.1	× 53
30.16	182	450.5

4.	5.	6.
5.19	4.07	0.384
× 37	× 0.7	× 8.3
192.03	2.849	3.1872

7.	8.	9.
42.5	0.15	1.36
× 24	× 0.3	× 2.4
1020	0.045	3.264

Round each number to the underlined place.

10. 5<u>9</u>37 _____5900_____   11. <u>2</u>7,592 _____30,000_____

12. 7,<u>6</u>84,908 ___7,700,000___   13. 28<u>1</u>2 _____2810_____

Solve.

14. The highest waterfall in the United States is Yosemite Falls. The waterfall has three sections: Upper Yosemite Falls measures 1430 feet, Cascades measures 675 feet, and Lower Yosemite measures 320 feet. What is the total height of Yosemite Falls?

_____2425 feet_____

Name _____

Estimate the product. Answers may vary. Ranges are given.

1. 139
    × 78
8000–11,000

2. $5.15
    ×   6
$30.00–$31.00

3. 83
    × 61
4800–5000

4. $7.10
    ×   4
$28–$29

5. 715
    × 39
27,000–28,000

6. $0.98
    ×   7
$6.50–$7.00

7. 4 × $4.06 ___$16___

8. 8 × $2.35 ___$16–$20___

9. 5.7 × 9.3 ___45–60___

10. 63 × 92 ___5400–6500___

Write the LCM.

11. 4 and 12 ___12___

12. 8 and 9 ___72___

13. 5 and 18 ___90___

14. 3, 5, and 8 ___120___

15. 2, 3, and 9 ___18___

16. 2, 5, and 6 ___30___

Solve.

17. Langston Hughes, a famous African-American writer, lived from 1902 to 1967. How many years did he live?

___65 years___

38 ▸ DAILY CUMULATIVE REVIEW

Write the answer. Use mental math.

1. 63 + 27 _____90_____   **2.** 96 − 67 _____29_____

3. 700 × 30 _____21,000_____   **4.** 3900 − 1600 _____2300_____

5. 300 × 50 _____15,000_____   **6.** $8.99 + $7.50 _____$16.49_____

Write each number in word form.

7. 6.68 _____six and sixty-eight hundredths_____

8. 0.015 _____fifteen thousandths_____

9. 7.009 _____seven and nine thousandths_____

10. 228.3 _____two hundred twenty-eight and three tenths_____

11. 92.06 _____ninety-two and six hundredths_____

12. 18.75 _____eighteen and seventy-five hundredths_____

13. 20.02 _____twenty and two hundredths_____

Solve.

14. When Phil is resting, his heart beats 72 times in a minute. At that rate, how many times does his heart beat in an hour?

4320 times

Write the product.

1. 8.66
    × 2.9

    25.114

2. 0.35
    × 0.07

    0.0245

3. 4.8
    × 2.2

    10.56

4. 0.52
    × 0.4

    0.208

5. 0.89
    × 0.02

    0.0178

6. 2.12
    × 9.8

    20.776

Round each number to the underlined place.

7. 6.7̲3 _____6.7_____

8. 1̲3.908 _____14_____

9. 6.2̲205 _____6.22_____

10. 0.48̲1 _____0.48_____

Read the problem. Then make notes or make a table to solve.

11. Randi is 4 years older than Tiffany. Tiffany is 12 years younger than Todd. If Todd is 16, what are the ages of Randi and Tiffany?

    Tiffany is 4 years old; Randi is 8 years old.

12. Adam is 9 years older than Jeff. Jeff is 7 years older than Ron. If Ron is 24 years old, what are the ages of Adam and Jeff?

    Jeff is 31 years old; Adam is 40 years old.

Name _____

Estimate.   Answers may vary. Ranges are given.

1. $5.05
    $\times\quad 4$
$20.00–$20.20

2.   518
      750
    $+\quad 43$
   1200–1300

3.   6.80
    $-\ 2.35$
   4.5–5

4.   5.9
     2.8
    $+\ 1.6$
   10–12

5.   644
    $\times\ 25$
  12,000–18,000

6.   14.13
    $-\quad 1.7$
     12–13

Solve.

7. $5a = 90$ _____ $a = 18$ _____

8. $9y = 36$ _____ $y = 4$ _____

9. $104 = 8d$ _____ $d = 13$ _____

10. $10t = 150$ _____ $t = 15$ _____

11. $17v = 119$ _____ $v = 7$ _____

12. $8d = 184$ _____ $d = 23$ _____

13. $7m = 133$ _____ $m = 19$ _____

14. $14n = 70$ _____ $n = 5$ _____

Solve.

15. A hummingbird egg weighs 0.0006 kilogram.
An ostrich egg weighs 1.4 kilograms. How much
more does the ostrich egg weigh than the
hummingbird egg?

1.3994 kilograms

Write the answer.

1. 597
    × 24
    ───
    14,328

2. 157 R1
    9) 1414

3. 7.132
    + 2.75
    ──────
    9.882

4. 9.4
    − 6.675
    ───────
    2.725

5. 310
    3) 930

6. 309
    × 14
    ────
    4326

Solve for the missing factor. Use mental math.

7. $50 \cdot h = 1000$ _____ $h = 20$ _____

8. $c \cdot 3 = 3000$ _____ $c = 1000$ _____

9. $q \cdot 4 = 1600$ _____ $q = 400$ _____

10. $v \cdot 90 = 18{,}000$ _____ $v = 200$ _____

Solve.

11. During one week Marvin worked for 17 hours as a carpenter's helper. How much did he earn for the week if his hourly wage is $5.50?

    _____ $93.50 _____

12. The next week Marvin was given a raise of $1 per hour. How much did he earn working 23 hours at his new wage?

    _____ $149.50 _____

42 DAILY CUMULATIVE REVIEW

Write the answer.

1. $39.61
+ 36.86
$76.47

2. $$4\overline{)708} = 177$$

3. 0.75
× 0.8
0.6

4. 3.8
× 0.6
2.28

5. 820.4
− 65.95
754.45

6. $$6\overline{)280} = 46\ R4$$

Write each word in standard form.

7. four and five tenths _____4.5_____

8. eighty-three thousandths _____0.083_____

9. sixteen and nine thousandths _____16.009_____

10. one hundred one and six hundredths _____101.06_____

11. two hundred forty and two hundredths _____240.02_____

12. one and one hundredth _____1.01_____

Solve.

13. Mrs. Fitzgerald is setting a weekly budget of $120 for food for her family. How much is her food budget for a year? _____$6240_____

Name _____

Answers may vary. Ranges are given.

Estimate the sum or difference.

1.
```
   9.6
   7.9
 + 4.7
 22–23
```

2.
```
   5.04
   4.55
 + 0.72
  10–11
```

3.
```
   $9.49
    3.39
 +  6.82
  $19–$20
```

4.
```
   8.05
 − 1.7
  6–6.5
```

5.
```
   4.51
 − 0.61
   3.5–4
```

6.
```
   7.9
 − 5.1
   2–3
```

Write the value of the multiplication expression.

7. $3m$ for $m = 4$; $m = 20$ _____ 12; 60

8. $k \cdot 12$ for $k = 9$; $k = 13$ _____ 108; 156

9. $9x$ for $x = 5$; $x = 23$ _____ 45; 207

10. $6w$ for $w = 21$; $w = 40$ _____ 126; 240

11. $8j$ for $j = 11$; $j = 15$ _____ 88; 120

12. $r \cdot 25$ for $r = 8$; $r = 25$ _____ 200; 625

Solve.

13. Scientists have identified about 13,300 species of saltwater fish and about 8400 species of freshwater fish. About how many more species of saltwater fish are there than freshwater fish?

about 4900 species

14. About how many species of fish have been identified in all?

about 21,700 species

44 DAILY CUMULATIVE REVIEW

Write the answer. Use mental math.

1. 2.3×10 ____23____

2. $\$0.81 \times 100$ ____$81____

3. $44 + 77$ ____121____

4. $830 - 440$ ____390____

5. 0.25×1000 ____250____

6. $100 + 580 + 420$ ____1100____

Solve. Look for ways to use mental math.

7. $n \div 6 = 18$ ____$n = 108$____

8. $45 = \frac{b}{10}$ ____$b = 450$____

9. $19 = g \div 7$ ____$g = 133$____

10. $\frac{p}{20} = 5$ ____$p = 100$____

Solve.

11. Rose cycled for 3 hours to cover a distance of 45 miles. What was her average speed?

____15 miles per hour____

12. Jake cycled 27 miles in 2 hours. How many miles does he have to cycle in the third hour to have the same average speed as Rose?

____18 miles____

Name _____

Write the answer.

1. 907
  × 86
  78,002

2. 17 R4
  7)123

3. 1.92
  − 0.112
  1.808

4. 1.77
  × 16
  28.32

5. 602.2
  + 16.63
  618.83

6. 19 R38
  48)950

7. 49.06
  − 22.83
  26.23

8. 6.05
  × 72
  435.6

9. 14 R21
  26)385

Write the value.

10. $(12 - 4) \times 20 =$ ___160___

11. $9 \times (2 + 7) \div 3 =$ ___27___

12. $8 - 3 \times 2 + 4 =$ ___6___

13. $10 \div 5 + 18 =$ ___20___

Solve.

14. In the spring, a queen bee can lay one
egg every 43 seconds. At that rate,
how many eggs can she lay in an hour?   ___83 eggs___

Name _____

Write the answer.

1. $\quad$ 7 R61
    80$\overline{)621}$

2. $\quad$ 35 R12
    16$\overline{)572}$

3. $\quad$ 79 R27
    43$\overline{)3424}$

4. $\quad$ 0.33
    $\times\,0.65$
    0.2145

5. $\quad$ 2.08
    $\times\,0.12$
    0.2496

6. $\quad$ 379
    $\times\;\;25$
    9475

7. $\quad$ 2.06
    $\times\,1.08$
    2.2248

8. $\quad$ 67.5
    $\times\,0.23$
    15.525

9. $\quad$ 5.63
    $\times\,2.01$
    11.3163

Write the quotient. Use mental math.

10. $800 \div 80$ $\qquad$ 10

11. $2500 \div 50$ $\qquad$ 50

12. $640 \div 8$ $\qquad$ 80

13. $14,000 \div 20$ $\qquad$ 700

14. $810 \div 9$ $\qquad$ 90

15. $56,000 \div 70$ $\qquad$ 800

Solve. $\qquad$ **Accept any reasonable answer.**

16. The blackpoll warbler, a North American bird, flies
nonstop nearly 2500 miles to its winter home in
South America. The journey takes about 90 hours.
Estimate the bird's average speed.

_____ 25 to 30 miles per hour _____

Name _____

Estimate the product.   Answers may vary. Ranges are given.

1. 17×9 ___150–200___

2. 45×38 ___1500–2000___

3. 77×15 ___1200–1600___

4. 304×9 ___2700–3040___

5. 7×81 ___560–800___

6. 28×16 ___450___

7. 5×592 ___2500–3000___

8. 64×52 ___3000–3200___

Round to the thousands place.

9. 8921 ___9000___

10. $74,606 ___$75,000___

11. 60,553 ___61,000___

12. 165,648 ___166,000___

13. $986 ___$1000___

14. 22,489 ___22,000___

15. 74,398 ___74,000___

16. 181,864 ___182,000___

Solve.

17. Megan worked 6 weeks during the summer as a camp counselor. She earned a total of $720. How much did she earn each week?   ___$120___

18. How much would Megan have earned if she had worked for 9 weeks at the same salary?   ___$1080___

Name _____

Estimate the quotient. Answers may vary. Ranges are given.

1. $\begin{array}{r} 80 \\ 3\overline{)\,245} \end{array}$

2. $\begin{array}{r} 20\text{–}30 \\ 26\overline{)\,690} \end{array}$

3. $\begin{array}{r} 450\text{–}500 \\ 8\overline{)\,3986} \end{array}$

4. $\begin{array}{r} 200\text{–}300 \\ 44\overline{)\,9580} \end{array}$

5. $\begin{array}{r} 7000\text{–}7200 \\ 6\overline{)\,42{,}822} \end{array}$

6. $\begin{array}{r} 100\text{–}200 \\ 54\overline{)\,9001} \end{array}$

7. $4818 \div 23$ ___200-240___

8. $3776 \div 4$ ___900-1000___

Complete each table.

9.

Mary's Age	Phil's Age
9	4
12	7
14	9
16	11
m	$m-5$

10.

Ticket Price in Dollars	Ticket Price with Coupon
20	12
32	24
39	31
50	42
t	$t-8$

Solve.

11. The picnic tables at the park can seat 8 students. If 70 students attend the class picnic, how many tables will be needed?

    9 tables

12. If 1 gallon of juice contains 20 servings, how many gallons are needed at the picnic for each student to have 2 servings?

    7 gallons

49 DAILY CUMULATIVE REVIEW

Write the answer.

1.	2.	3.
6.4	62	$12.81
1.01	− 7.042	7.03
+ 0.03	54.958	+ 8.12
7.44		$27.96

4.	5.	6.
9.06	669.5	315.08
− 8.579	+ 123.6	− 203.6
0.481	793.1	111.48

Write the LCM.

7. 3 and 14 ___42___

8. 3, 5, and 18 ___90___

9. 2, 5, and 6 ___30___

10. 2, 3, and 5 ___30___

11. 12 and 20 ___60___

12. 4, 6, and 7 ___84___

Solve.

13. For a school fund-raiser, the student council plans to sell peanuts in 2-ounce packages. How many ounces of peanuts do they need to buy in order to make 120 packages of peanuts? ___240 ounces___

14. How many pounds of peanuts is that? ___15 pounds___

15. If they buy the peanuts for $1.79 per pound and they sell each 2-ounce package for 39¢, how much profit will they earn? ___$19.95___

Name _____

50 ⟩ DAILY CUMULATIVE REVIEW

Write the answer.

1. 94
    × 89
    8366

2. 213 R1
    3)640

3. 75 yd
    9)675 yd

4. 49.2
    + 22.73
    71.93

5. 180.09
    − 26.1
    153.99

6. 212
    × 167
    35,404

Write the missing decimals to complete the pattern.

7. 0.1, 0.3, 0.5, ___0.7___, ___0.9___, ___1.1___

8. 10.75, 10.76, 10.77, ___10.78___, ___10.79___, ___10.80___

9. 3.9, 4.9, 5.9, ___6.9___, ___7.9___, ___8.9___

10. 3.48, 3.50, 3.52, ___3.54___, ___3.56___, ___3.58___

Solve.

11. For her 4-H club project, Katie keeps
    track of how many eggs she collects
    from her 16 chickens each day. In
    November, she collected 304 eggs.
    On average, how many eggs did each
    chicken lay during the month?   ___19 eggs___

51 DAILY CUMULATIVE REVIEW

Write the answer. Use mental math.

1. $62 + 89$ ___151___

2. $\$5.00 + \$2.99$ ___$7.99___

3. $760 - 95$ ___665___

4. $668 - 298$ ___370___

5. $350 + 96$ ___446___

6. $640 + 270$ ___910___

7. $\$6.50 + 3.99$ ___$10.49___

8. $570 - 430$ ___140___

Round each number to the underlined place.

9. 8.2̲93 ___8.3___

10. 9.39̲54 ___9.40___

11. 31̲.097 ___31___

12. 0.02̲18 ___0.02___

13. 5.60̲3 ___5.60___

14. 8.4̲15 ___8.4___

15. 26̲.85 ___27___

16. 42.2̲8 ___42.3___

Complete the table.

17.

Number of Inches	Feet
24	24 ÷ 12, or 2
48	48 ÷ 12, or 4
60	60 ÷ 12, or 5
72	72 ÷ 12, or 6
s	$s \div 12$

52 DAILY CUMULATIVE REVIEW

Write the answer.

1.
$$\begin{array}{r} 37 \\ \times\ 22 \\ \hline 814 \end{array}$$

2. $4\overline{)90}$ **22 R2**

3. $9\overline{)54,581}$ **6064 R5**

4.
$$\begin{array}{r} 165 \\ \times\ 61 \\ \hline 10,065 \end{array}$$

5. $2\overline{)1237}$ **618 R1**

6.
$$\begin{array}{r} 755 \\ \times\ 270 \\ \hline 203,850 \end{array}$$

7. 81×937 ____**75,897**____

8. $1991 \div 7$ ____**284 R3**____

Write _prime_ or _composite_ to describe each number.

9. 67 ____**prime**____

10. 96 ____**composite**____

11. 85 ____**composite**____

12. 101 ____**prime**____

13. 97 ____**prime**____

14. 143 ____**composite**____

Solve.

15. Kristen keeps a record of her science test scores. Her scores this semester are 88, 75, 92, and 85. What is her average science test score this semester?

____**85**____

Name _____

 53 **DAILY CUMULATIVE REVIEW**
••

Estimate each sum or difference.

Answers may vary.
Ranges are given.

1. 809 + 733 + 190   1700

2. 199 + 654 + 77   900–1000

3. 8395 – 3076   5000–5500

4. 7345 – 5900   1000–1500

5. $4.51 + $4.90 + $0.87 $10–$11

6. 8.6 m + 0.5 m + 1.8 m   10.5 m–11 m

Write each word in standard form.

7. two and four hundredths   2.04

8. thirty-eight and fifty-four thousandths   38.054

9. two hundred forty-two ten-thousandths   0.0242

10. one hundred three and nine tenths   103.9

Solve.

11. The longest river in the world, the Nile,
    is 4150 miles in length. The Mississippi-
    Missouri river system is 3872 miles long.
    How much longer is the Nile?   278 miles

Name _____

Write the answer.

1. 9.5
    × 6
    ⎯⎯
    57

2. 4.03
    × 0.24
    ⎯⎯⎯
    0.9672

3. 7.23
    × 3.5
    ⎯⎯⎯
    25.305

4. $\overset{170}{18\overline{)3060}}$

5. $\overset{28\ R42}{60\overline{)1722}}$

6. $\overset{12\ R36}{47\overline{)600}}$

7. 38 × 0.65 _____24.7_____

8. 735 ft ÷ 49 _____15 ft_____

List each group of numbers from least to greatest.
Then find the range, mean, median, and mode.

9. 44, 47, 49, 51, 44, 53 _____44, 44, 47, 49, 51, 53;_____
   range: 9; mean: 48; median: 48; mode: 44

10. 14, 12, 5, 4, 10 _____4, 5, 10, 12, 14;_____
    range: 10; mean: 9; median: 10; mode: none

11. $323, $409, $358, $378 _____$323, $358, $378, $409;_____
    range: $86; mean: $367; median: $368; mode: none

12. 256, 362, 104, 362 _____104, 256, 362, 362;_____
    range: 258; mean: 271; median: 309; mode: 362

55 ⟩ DAILY CUMULATIVE REVIEW

Solve. Use mental math.

1. 30×100 _____ 3000

2. 600×5 _____ 3000

3. $12 \times 25 \times 4$ _____ 1200

4. 40×40 _____ 1600

5. $7 \times 5 \times 2 \times 7$ _____ 490

6. $9 \times 2 \times 50$ _____ 900

Write the value.

7. $40 + 2 \div 1$

_____ 42

8. $(15 - 9) \times 4$

_____ 24

9. $3 + 9 \times 7$

_____ 66

10. $(1 + 5) \div 2 + 13$

_____ 16

11. $6 \div 3 + 8 - 1$

_____ 9

12. $17 + 9 \times 4 - 5$

_____ 48

13. $9 - (2 \times 3)$

_____ 3

14. $5 \div 5 \times 10 + 4$

_____ 14

Solve.

15. In Alaska, the Iditarod Trail Sled Dog Race from Anchorage to Nome is 1158 miles long. In 1990, Susan Butcher won the race in just over 11 days. About how many miles did she average each day?

_____ **about 100 miles**

Name _____

Write the answer.

1. $\begin{array}{r} 1.06 \\ \times\ \ 30 \\ \hline 31.8 \end{array}$

2. $\begin{array}{r} 265.6 \\ +\ \ 90.2 \\ \hline 355.8 \end{array}$

3. $\begin{array}{r} \$26.03 \\ -\ \ \ 7.78 \\ \hline \$18.25 \end{array}$

4. $7\overline{)8790}$ 1255 R5

5. $\begin{array}{r} 0.057 \\ \times\ \ \ 0.2 \\ \hline 0.0114 \end{array}$

6. $30\overline{)3784}$ 126 R4

**Write the prime factorization of each number. If a
number is prime, write the word *prime*.**

Order of listings
may vary.

7. 44

$2 \times 2 \times 11$

8. 75

$3 \times 5 \times 5$

9. 83

prime

10. 95

5×19

11. 66

$2 \times 3 \times 11$

12. 105

$3 \times 5 \times 7$

Solve.

13. In the 1990 U.S. census, California was the most
    populous state with 29,279,000 residents. To the
    nearest million, about how many people live in
    California?

    about 29,000,000 people

Name _____

Divide. Look for ways to use mental math.

1. $7\overline{)498}$ $\overset{71}{}$ R1

2. $5\overline{)656}$ $\overset{131}{}$ R1

3. $4\overline{)3206}$ $\overset{801}{}$ R2

4. $39\overline{)7365}$ $\overset{188}{}$ R33

5. $17\overline{)1652}$ $\overset{97}{}$ R3

6. $24\overline{)4826}$ $\overset{201}{}$ R2

7. $755 \div 10$ ___75 R5___

8. $6018 \div 6$ ___1003___

Write the greatest common factor (GCF) for each pair of numbers.

9. 30 and 45 ___15___

10. 5 and 13 ___1___

11. 9 and 18 ___9___

12. 24 and 44 ___4___

13. 26 and 65 ___13___

14. 18 and 39 ___3___

Solve.

15. Melissa has 4 cats. She feeds each cat 4 ounces of dry cat food each day. Will a 5-pound bag of cat food last for a week of feeding?   ___no___

Name _____

58 DAILY CUMULATIVE REVIEW

Write the answer.

1.
$$\begin{array}{r} 559 \\ \times\ \ 0.5 \\ \hline 279.5 \end{array}$$

2.
$$\begin{array}{r} \$57.84 \\ +\ \ 38.63 \\ \hline \$96.47 \end{array}$$

3. $\overset{38\ R67}{75\overline{)2917}}$

4.
$$\begin{array}{r} 8.51 \\ \times\ \ 4.1 \\ \hline 34.891 \end{array}$$

5.
$$\begin{array}{r} 774.30 \\ -\ \ 41.84 \\ \hline 732.46 \end{array}$$

6. $\overset{67\ R6}{94\overline{)6304}}$

7. $9.2 + 0.39 + 0.02$ ____9.61____   **8.** $0.528 - 0.19$ ____0.338____

Solve. Look for ways to use mental math.

9. $4r = 96$ ____$r = 24$____   **10.** $10 = f \div 13$ ____$f = 130$____

11. $g \div 68 = 5$ ____$g = 340$____   **12.** $88 = 8y$ ____$y = 11$____

Solve.

13. Marianna wants to make a set of placemats. Each placemat requires 1 yard of fabric. If she has 15 feet of fabric, how many placemats can she make?

_____ **5 placemats** _____

Name _____

··

Estimate the quotient. Answers may vary. Ranges are given.

1. $\underline{90-100}$
   $5\overline{)470}$

2. $\underline{2-3}$
   $69\overline{)168}$

3. $\underline{4000-5000}$
   $4\overline{)18,093}$

4. $\underline{50-70}$
   $38\overline{)2048}$

5. $\underline{500-600}$
   $8\overline{)4435}$

6. $\underline{200-300}$
   $25\overline{)6014}$

7. $42,217 \div 6$ ___7000–7500___

8. $2453 \div 53$ ___45–50___

Round to the nearest tenth.

9. 2.04 _____2.0_____

10. 17.866 _____17.9_____

11. 6.39 _____6.4_____

12. 50.538 _____50.5_____

Solve.

13. Saul wants to buy a leash, a collar, and some treats for his dog. He has $25 to spend. What can he buy?

Item	Cost
nylon leash	$12.89
leather leash	$18.50
leather collar	$ 8.95
dog treats, 1 lb	$ 2.39
dog treats, 3 lb	$ 6.05

_____One possible answer: nylon leash,_____

_____leather collar, and dog treats, 1 lb_____

Name _____

Write the answer.

1. 5.62
   + 0.348
   _____
    5.968

2. 96,442
   − 2,919
   _____
    93,523

3. $12.71
   + 10.52
   _____
    $23.23

4. 0.875
   − 0.1989
   _____
    0.6761

5. $190.10
   −   58.02
   _____
    $132.08

6. 70
   − 6.73
   _____
    63.27

7. 3.1 + 9.03 + 0.86

   _____12.99_____

8. 52 + 3.5 + 150

   _____205.5_____

Write the value.

9. (1 + 3) × 5

   _____20_____

10. (9 + 9) ÷ 3 + 6

   _____12_____

11. 3 + 8 ÷ 2 + 3

   _____10_____

12. 8 − 5 × (0 + 1)

   _____3_____

**Read the problem. Then, write the information
needed to solve the problem. Write several ways
to find the information.** Answers may vary.

13. Mrs. Tena wants a potato casserole to be baked
   at 6:00 P.M. What time should she put it in the
   oven?

   Needed information: length of time it takes to cook

   the casserole; look in a cookbook; ask a friend

61 DAILY CUMULATIVE REVIEW

New England States Electoral Vote

Maine	🖐 🖐 🖐 🖐
	🖐 = 1 electoral vote
Vermont	🖐 🖐 🖐
New Hampshire	🖐 🖐 🖐 🖐
Massachusetts	🖐 🖐 🖐 🖐 🖐 🖐 🖐 🖐 🖐 🖐 🖐 🖐 🖐
Connecticut	🖐 🖐 🖐 🖐 🖐 🖐 🖐 🖐
Rhode Island	🖐 🖐 🖐 🖐

Write the answer. Use the graph.

1. Which New England state has the greatest number of electoral votes?

   Massachusetts

2. How many electoral votes do the New England states have in all?

   36 votes

3. Which New England state has 8 electoral votes?

   Connecticut

4. Together, do Maine, Vermont, and New Hampshire have as many electoral votes as Massachusetts?

   no

5. Which New England states have the same number of electoral votes?

   Maine, New Hampshire, and Rhode Island

Name _____

Write the answer.

1.
$$\begin{array}{r} 0.268 \\ \times\quad 52 \\ \hline 13.936 \end{array}$$

2.
$$\begin{array}{r} 662 \text{ yd} \\ 7\overline{)4634 \text{ yd}} \end{array}$$

3.
$$\begin{array}{r} 11,001 \\ 4\overline{)44,004} \end{array}$$

4.
$$\begin{array}{r} 53.15 \\ \times\quad 144 \\ \hline 7653.6 \end{array}$$

5.
$$\begin{array}{r} 12.7 \\ \times\quad 88 \\ \hline 1117.6 \end{array}$$

6.
$$\begin{array}{r} 23 \text{ R8} \\ 21\overline{)491} \end{array}$$

7. 9.078×358 ___3249.924___   **8.** $3000 \div 34$ ___88 R8___

Write the prime factorization of each number.

9. 60 ___$2 \times 2 \times 3 \times 5$___

10. 180 ___$2 \times 2 \times 3 \times 3 \times 5$___

11. 306 ___$2 \times 3 \times 3 \times 17$___

Solve.

12. Martha helps her mother with chores on Saturdays. Her mother pays her $3 an hour. Martha worked for 4 hours on each of the last 4 Saturdays. How much did she earn?

___$48___

63 DAILY CUMULATIVE REVIEW

Write the answer. Use mental math.

1. 30×70

2100

2. $60 \div 3$

20

3. $81 + 69$

150

4. 16×1000

16,000

5. $93 \div 3$

31

6. $\$7.43 - \$2.99$

$4.44

7. $68 \div 2$

34

8. 21×4

84

9. $4 \times 80 \times 10$

3200

List each group of numbers from least to greatest. Then find the range, mean, median, and mode.

10. 70, 93, 67, 60, 80   60, 67, 70, 80, 93;

range: 33; mean: 74; median: 70; mode: none

11. 9, 19, 27, 19, 27, 19   9, 19, 19, 19, 27, 27;

range: 18; mean: 20; median: 19; mode: 19

12. $794, $703, $863, $944 $703, $794, $863, $944;

range: 241; mean: $826; median: $828.50; mode: none

Name _____

**Saylor Family
Annual Budget**

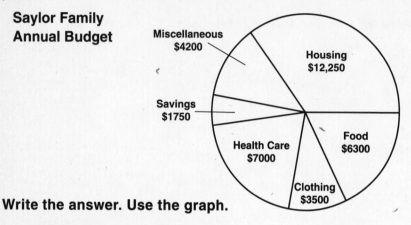

Write the answer. Use the graph.

1. Which category is largest in the
   Saylor family annual budget?

   housing

2. What is the total annual budget?

   $35,000

3. What is the difference between the
   amount in the largest category and
   the amount in the smallest category?

   $10,500

4. Do health care, clothing, and food make up more
   or less than half the Saylor family annual budget?

   less than half

5. What two categories make up more than half the
   annual budget?

   housing and food or housing and health care

6. What do you think might be included in the
   miscellaneous category?

   Answers may vary. Sample answer:

   entertainment, gifts, books

Name _____

....

Divide.

1. $\overset{10}{14\overline{)140}}$

2. $\overset{8}{66\overline{)528}}$

3. $\overset{135\ R42}{48\overline{)6522}}$

4. $\overset{38\ R11}{15\overline{)581}}$

5. $\overset{15\ R44}{50\overline{)794}}$

6. $\overset{1080\ R1}{4\overline{)4321}}$

7. $3552 \div 71$ ___50 R2___

8. $1515 \div 15$ ___101___

Solve.

9. $a \div 3 = 27$ ___$a = 81$___

10. $7n = 70$ ___$n = 10$___

11. $15 = c \div 5$ ___$c = 75$___

12. $72 = 12s$ ___$s = 6$___

Read the problem. Then make notes, make a table, or use other strategies to solve.

13. Admission to the Fun and Sun Water Park is $16.25 for an adult and $9.95 for a child under 12. There are 3 children in the Schoel family. Susan is 8, Scott is 12, and Cindy is 14 years old. If both parents and all 3 children go to the park, how much will admission cost the Schoels?

___$74.95___

Name _____

66 DAILY CUMULATIVE REVIEW

Estimate each answer. Answers may vary. Ranges are given.

1. 115 + 97 + 183

400–425

2. 607 × 27

15000–18,000

3. 2717 − 1350

1300–2000

4. 9 × 817

7200–8000

5. 7 × $6.92

$48–$49

6. 2.5 + 1.64 + 0.19

4–5

Round each number to the underlined place.

7. 95,527   100,000

8. 5820   5800

9. 3,403,452   3,000,000

10. 19,216,807   19,217,000

Read the problem. Then make notes, make a table, or use other strategies to solve.

11. Meredith wants to bake yeast rolls for dinner. She wants the rolls to be done by 5:30 P.M. It takes 30 minutes to mix the dough, and the rolls must rise for 1 hour and 15 minutes. Then the rolls need to bake for 20 minutes. What time should she start the rolls?

3:25 P.M.

Name _____

 67 DAILY CUMULATIVE REVIEW

Write the answer.

1. 66
    × 41
    ____
    2706

2. 860 R10
    11)9470

3. 340 R25
    29)9885

4. 2.074
    + 0.4129
    _____
    2.4869

5. 0.52
    × 157
    _____
    81.64

6. 38.12
    − 13.83
    _____
    24.29

7. 8.6
    + 7.5
    ____
    16.1

8. 8.68
    × 1.05
    _____
    9.114

9. 4 R2
    62)250

In which number does the digit 2 have the greater value?

10. a. 9072   b. 5257   _____b_____

11. a. 23,189   b. 192,806   _____a_____

12. a. 125,193   b. 752,745   _____a_____

Solve.

13. In 1988 there were 40,192,386 elementary and secondary students in the United States. How many students is that to the nearest hundred thousand?

40,200,000 students

Name _____

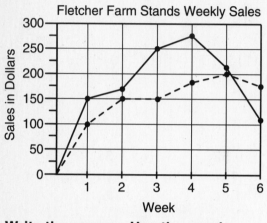

Fletcher Farm Stands Weekly Sales

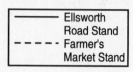

—— Ellsworth Road Stand
– – – Farmer's Market Stand

Write the answer. Use the graph.

1. During which week did the farm stand on Ellsworth Road sell the most produce?

   week 4

2. What were the greatest combined weekly sales for the two stands?

   _$455_

3. In which week were sales greater at the Farmer's Market stand?

   week 6

4. Which stand generally had higher sales?

   Ellsworth Road Stand

5. The stand on Ellsworth Road is open 6 days a week. The stand at Farmer's Market is open only 3 days a week. Which stand do you think is more profitable? Why?

   Answers may vary. Sample answer: The Farmer's

   Market Stand. It is open half as much as the other stand,

   but makes almost as much money.

69 ▶ DAILY CUMULATIVE REVIEW

Write the product. You may use a calculator.

1.   805
 $\times$ 591
 475,755

2.   1789
 $\times$ 654
 1,170,006

3.   9035
 $\times$ 286
 2,584,010

4.   1,905,927
 $\times$ 58
 110,543,766

5.   45,167
 $\times$ 3500
 158,084,500

6.   44,700,000
 $\times$ 213
 9,521,100,000

Write each number in word form.

7. 0.97 _____ ninety–seven hundredths _____

8. 3.606 ____ three and six hundred six thousandths ____

9. 0.0019 _____ nineteen ten-thousandths _____

10. 12.036 ____ twelve and thirty-six thousandths ____

Solve.

11. Andina wants to buy a new bicycle that costs $89.95. She saves $1.50 a week. Will she be able to save enough for the bicycle in one year?

_____ no _____

12. Fatima practices the piano for 30 minutes each school day and an hour on Saturday. How many minutes does she practice in a week?

_____ 210 minutes _____

Name _____

Write the answer.

1. $\begin{array}{r} 6779 \\ + 1594 \\ \hline 8373 \end{array}$

2. $\begin{array}{r} 5.025 \\ - 0.439 \\ \hline 4.586 \end{array}$

3. $9\overline{)362}$ 40 R2

4. $\begin{array}{r} 397 \\ \times\ 28 \\ \hline 11,116 \end{array}$

5. $\begin{array}{r} \$323.08 \\ -\ 25.74 \\ \hline \$297.34 \end{array}$

6. $\begin{array}{r} 891 \\ \times\ 30 \\ \hline 26,730 \end{array}$

Write the greatest common factor (GCF) for each pair of numbers.

7. 6, 28 ____2____

8. 4, 50 ____2____

9. 7, 26 ____1____

10. 21, 91 ____7____

11. 39, 65 ____13____

12. 40, 72 ____8____

Solve. Use simpler numbers, make a plan, or use other strategies that help you.

13. In 1989, 731,013 passenger cars and 280,970 trucks and buses were manufactured in Brazil. During the same year, 330,492 passenger cars and 27,772 trucks and buses were manufactured in Australia. How many more vehicles were manufactured in Brazil than in Australia?

_____653,719 vehicles_____

Name _____

Find the quotient. Write it as a decimal.

1. $6 \div 8$ _____0.75_____

2. $60 \div 80$ _____0.75_____

3. $0.6 \div 8$ _____0.075_____

4. $5\overline{)8}$ 1.6

5. $8\overline{)5}$ 0.625

6. $80\overline{)500}$ 6.25

7. $\frac{5}{20}$ _____0.25_____

8. $\frac{20}{5}$ _____4_____

9. $\frac{5}{25}$ _____0.2_____

Write the value of each expression.

10. $9(p)$ for $p = 4$, $p = 8$, $p = 15$ _____36; 72; 135_____

11. $6s$ for $s = 6$, $s = 10$, $s = 25$ _____36; 60; 150_____

12. $r \cdot 7$ for $r = 3$, $r = 11$, $r = 40$ _____21; 77; 280_____

13. $5 \cdot t + 2$ for $t = 8$, $t = 12$ _____42; 62_____

14. $1.5n$ for $n = 10$, $n = 0.8$ _____15; 1.2_____

Solve.

15. Ruth makes gift baskets of fruit. Each basket
contains 3 pieces of fruit. She uses apples,
bananas, oranges, and pears. If she always uses
3 different fruits in a basket, how many different
baskets can she make?

4 baskets; apple, banana, pear; apple, banana, orange;
apple, orange, pear; banana, orange, pear

Name _____

DAILY CUMULATIVE REVIEW

Write the product.

1.
```
  3.3
× 8.6
─────
28.38
```

2.
```
  9.18
×   10
─────
 91.8
```

3.
```
  0.81
×  0.8
─────
 0.648
```

4.
```
  6.23
×  100
─────
  623
```

5.
```
  0.005
×   0.9
──────
 0.0045
```

6.
```
  9.07
×  4.4
──────
39.908
```

7. 0.29 × 100

    _____29_____

8. 5.8 × 2.1

    _____12.18_____

9. 4.03 × 11.2

    _____45.136_____

**Write an expression for each situation. Tell what
the variable stands for.**   Accept any reasonable expression.

10. Ryan spends 20 minutes grooming each horse.
The total number of minutes he spends grooming
horses =

   $h \cdot 20$; h = the number of horses
   _____

11. Jack spent $9 at the shopping mall. The amount
of money he has left =

   $m - \$9$; m = the amount of money Jack started with
   _____

12. Mrs. Schulz parked her car in the airport parking
lot for 8 days. The total cost of parking =

   $8 \cdot p$; p = the cost of parking per day
   _____

Name _____

Solve. Use mental math.

1. $4.5 \div 10$ ___0.45___

2. $72 \div 100$ ___0.72___

3. 9.1×10 ___91___

4. 7.14×100 ___714___

5. $82.2 \div 100$ ___0.822___

6. $306 \div 100$ ___3.06___

Name the tenths decimal that each number is closest to.

7. 0.49 ___0.5___   8. 8.51 ___8.5___   9. 17.42 ___17.4___

10. 1.04 ___1.0___   11. 9.37 ___9.4___   12. 25.26 ___25.3___

13. 313.1 ___313.1___   14. 45.08 ___45.1___   15. 0.95 ___1.0___

Solve.

16. The waiters and waitresses at the Green Garden Cafe pool their tips and share them equally. Shari collected $35.25 in tips; Phil collected $27.40; Sam collected $19.74; and Angie collected $25.95. Rounded to the nearest cent, how much tip money will each take home?

___$27.09___

17. Marsha bought supplies to make decorated T-shirts. She bought fabric paints for $17.95, Six T-shirts for $5.50 each, a bottle of glue for $2.95, and glitter for $1.85. How much did she spend in all?

___$55.75___

74 DAILY CUMULATIVE REVIEW

Write the answer.

1. 6.1
   × 0.5
   _____
   3.05

2. $15\overline{)960}$
   64

3. $27\overline{)1028}$
   38 R2

4. 18.86
   − 3.59
   _____
   15.27

5. 0.67
   + 0.098
   _____
   0.768

6. 0.29
   × 0.4
   _____
   0.116

Write the LCM.

7. 2, 3, and 8 ___24___

8. 5, 20, and 25 ___100___

9. 8, 10, and 16 ___80___

10. 5, 7, and 10 ___70___

Solve.

11. The Center City Historical Society collected $1075 for annual membership dues. If there are 86 members, how much did each member pay in dues? ___$12.50___

12. Last year the Historical Society budgeted $600 for an entry in the Founder's Day Parade. They spent $257 to rent a stagecoach, $225 on fabric for costumes, $39 for flowers, and $25 for balloons. Did they stay within their budget? ___yes___

Name _____

Students in the physical fitness club measured their pulse rates. The results are shown below. Use the information to complete exercises 1–7.

Student	Pulse	Student	Pulse	Student	Pulse	Student	Pulse
Hal	65	Carmen	65	Derek	62	Hoshi	72
Travis	75	Mavis	67	Martha	71	Bobby	70
Rosie	70	Darius	63	Dick	72	Tommy	71
Cora	68	Kim	80	Lisa	71	Dave	68

1. Complete the line-plot.

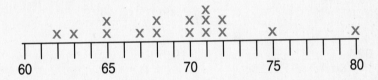

2. How many students measured their pulse?

16 students

3. How many students have a pulse of 71?

3 students

4. What is the lowest pulse rate recorded?

62

5. What is the highest pulse rate recorded?

80

6. How many students have a pulse rate of 70 or lower?

9 students

7. How many students have a pulse between 66 and 74?

10 students

76 DAILY CUMULATIVE REVIEW

Write the answer.

1.
```
   4.4
   1.06
 + 6.62
  12.08
```

2.
```
   0.95
   0.066
 + 1.82
   2.836
```

3.
```
   829.9
    18.32
 + 179.98
  1028.20
```

4.
```
      5.73
 16) 91.68
```

5.
```
     3.1
 7) 21.7
```

6.
```
      43.4
 3) 130.2
```

Round each number to the underlined place.

7. 2.246̲8 ___2.247___

8. 0.6̲37 ___0.6___

9. 6̲2.024 ___62___

10. 19.59̲36 ___19.59___

Use the information in the chart to solve.

11. Mrs. Fong bought 3 pounds of halibut for dinner. How much did she spend?

    ___$20.85___

Fish	Price per Pound
Haddock	$3.99
Halibut	$6.95
Cod	$2.50
Trout	$5.95

12. Mr. Gelman bought 1 pound of haddock and 1 pound of cod to make a fish chowder. How much did he spend?

    ___$6.49___

13. Ms. Debo bought 2 pounds of each kind of fish to make fish stew for a party. How much did she spend?

    ___$38.78___

Name _____

 77 **DAILY CUMULATIVE REVIEW**
∙∙∙

Estimate the answer. Answers may vary. Ranges are given.

1. $9 \times \$0.89$

   $\$8–\$9$

2. $6 \times \$5.14$

   $\$30–\$31$

3. $8411 \div 26$

   $300–400$

4. $37,079 \div 42$

   $900–1000$

5. $8 \times \$3.83$

   $\$24–\$32$

6. $5 \times \$0.69$

   $\$3.50–\$5$

Use the diagram to solve. You may use squared paper.

7. Ramesh's garden measures 15 feet by 15 feet. The paths through the garden are 3 feet wide. All 4 planting beds are the same size. What are the dimensions of each planting bed?

   6 feet by 6 feet

Ramesh's Garden

A	B
path	
C	D

8. Each plant in beds A and D needs a growing space of 1 foot by 1 foot. How many plants can be planted in beds A and D?

   72 plants

9. Each plant in beds B and C needs a growing space of 2 feet by 2 feet. How many plants can be planted in each of these beds?

   9 plants

Name _____

Estimate the quotient.   Answers may vary. Ranges are given.

$0.80–$1.00 $0.80–$1.00 $5.00–$6.00
1. 6)$5.11   **2.** 4)$3.52   **3.** 8)$44.38

$1.00–$2.00 $3.00–$4.00 $1.00–$2.00
4. 7)$12.04   **5.** 9)$28.19   **6.** 5)$6.46

Compare. Write < or >.

7. $1.15 ÷ 2 ⟩ $0.50   **8.** $6.35 ÷ 4 ⟨ $2.00

9. $6.79 ÷ 7 ⟨ $1.00   **10.** $2.49 ÷ 8 ⟩ $0.25

11. $3.39 ÷ 5 ⟨ $0.70   **12.** $206.47 ÷ 8 ⟩ $25.00

Estimate to find the better buy. Write a or b.

13. __b__   **a.** 1 apple for $0.50
                     b. 3 apples for $1.00

14. __b__   **a.** 10 pounds of laundry soap for $8.00
                     b. 2 pounds of laundry soap for $1.50

15. __b__   **a.** 1 pound tomatoes for $0.79
                     b. 5 pounds tomatoes for $3.00

16. __a__   **a.** 1 box of strawberries for $0.59
                     b. 12 boxes of strawberries for $8.00

In which number does the digit 6 have the greater value?

1. **a.** 9836   **b.** 9683   _b_

2. **a.** 62,075   **b.** 75,246   _a_

3. **a.** 3.061   **b.** 3.61   _b_

4. **a.** 25,687   **b.** 27,865   _a_

For a science project, Elena and José recorded the number of days it took different seeds to germinate. They want to display a bar graph showing the variation.

Seed	Days	Seed	Days
Parsley	12	Coriander	10
Basil	6	Oat	3
Wheat	3	Alfalfa	2
Bean	2	Pepper	did not germinate

5. Use the information in the chart to complete the bar graph.

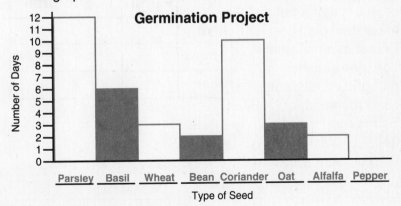

Germination Project

Name _____

Divide. Round the quotient to the given place.

1. tenths   91.8 ÷ 8   <u>11.5</u>

2. hundredths   227.03 ÷ 17   <u>13.35</u>

3. cent $41.83 ÷ 2   <u>$20.92</u>

4. thousandths   10.05 ÷ 9   <u>1.117</u>

5. tenths   34.6 ÷ 13   <u>2.7</u>

6. thousandths   18.415 ÷ 8   <u>2.302</u>

7. hundredths   62 ÷ 7   <u>8.86</u>

8. cent $798.59 ÷ 9   <u>$88.73</u>

Use the clues to solve the puzzle.

9. Liya, Emma, and Juan each brought a pet to the school pet show. One student brought a dog, one student brought a turtle, and one brought a parrot. Emma's pet is not a turtle. Liya's pet can fly. Who brought which pet?

	Parrot	Dog	Turtle
Liya			
Emma			
Juan			

<u>Liya: parrot; Emma: dog; Juan: turtle</u>

Name _____

Write the answer.

1. 60
     × 21
    ─────
    1260

2. $59.36
     +   1.23
    ─────────
     $60.59

3. 5)23.5 → 4.7

4. 9.41
     − 3.045
    ────────
     6.365

5. 17)853.4 → 50.2

6. 90.6
     × 0.8
    ───────
     72.48

7. 0.9 × 1.75

    1.575

8. 0.7 × 0.8

    0.56

9. 3.1 + 0.9 + 2.9

    6.9

Write *prime* or *composite* to describe each number.

10. 58

    composite

11. 37

    prime

12. 99

    composite

13. 19

    prime

14. 67

    prime

15. 105

    composite

Solve.

16. In 1989, United States dairy products consumption averaged 273.2 pounds per person per year. At that rate, about how many pounds of dairy products would a family of 5 consume in a year?

    1366 pounds

Name _____

82 DAILY CUMULATIVE REVIEW

Write the quotient.

1. $0.3\overline{)9.3}$ quotient: 31

2. $0.6\overline{)1.26}$ quotient: 2.1

3. $0.15\overline{)1.515}$ quotient: 10.1

4. $1.2\overline{)0.24}$ quotient: 0.2

5. $0.5\overline{)4.515}$ quotient: 9.03

6. $0.08\overline{)3.2}$ quotient: 40

7. $0.48 \div 0.4$
   __1.2__

8. $6.3 \div 0.09$
   __70__

9. $0.225 \div 0.06$
   __3.75__

Write the equivalent measure. Use the table of measures in the Data Book section of your math book.

10. 72 in. = __6__ ft

11. 5 yd = __15__ ft

12. 32 fl oz = __4__ c

13. 4 lb = __64__ oz

Solve.

14. At the hardware store, Marvin bought a box of 25 bolts for $10.50. What was the cost of each bolt?   __$0.42__

15. Marvin also bought a case of 12 fluorescent light bulbs on sale for $22.44. What was the cost of each bulb?   __$1.87__

83 DAILY CUMULATIVE REVIEW

Estimate the answer.

Accept any reasonable answer.
Samples are provided.

1. 23.6 + 16.4

_35–40_

2. 6 × 79

_480–500_

3. 212.7 – 13.52

_180–200_

4. 2628 ÷ 4

_600–700_

5. 648 + 425

_1000–1100_

6. 27 × 90

_2500–2700_

7. 36.71 – 14.5

_20–30_

8. 8026 ÷ 61

_100–200_

9. 16 × 33

_450–600_

Find the perimeter of each figure.

10.
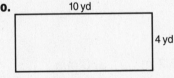
10 yd

4 yd

_28 yd_

11.
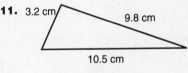
3.2 cm

9.8 cm

10.5 cm

_23.5 cm_

12.

6 ft

_24 ft_

13.
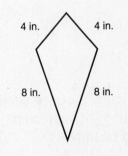
4 in.   4 in.

8 in.   8 in.

_24 in._

Name _____

Write the answer.

1.
$$\begin{array}{r} 0.139 \\ + 0.888 \\ \hline 1.027 \end{array}$$

2.
$$\begin{array}{r} 69.3 \\ - 20.911 \\ \hline 48.389 \end{array}$$

3.
$$\begin{array}{r} 181 \\ \times 17 \\ \hline 3077 \end{array}$$

4.
$$16\overline{)9.92} = 0.62$$

5.
$$\begin{array}{r} 11.9 \\ \times 0.21 \\ \hline 2.499 \end{array}$$

6.
$$9\overline{)31.5} = 3.5$$

7. $3.2 + 0.09 + 14$

   $\underline{\quad 17.29 \quad}$

8. 96×0.5

   $\underline{\quad 48 \quad}$

9. $30.05 - 14.68$

   $\underline{\quad 15.37 \quad}$

Complete. Write <, >, or = .

10. 4 L $\boxed{>}$ 400 mL

11. 8.7 m $\boxed{>}$ 870 mm

12. 0.1 kg $\boxed{<}$ 1000 g

13. 1.6 m $\boxed{=}$ 160 cm

14. 2600 g $\boxed{=}$ 2.6 kg

15. 510 mL $\boxed{>}$ 0.5 L

Solve.

16. How many 6-ounce servings of juice could be poured from 1 gallon of juice? How much juice would be left?

   $\underline{\quad \text{21 servings; 2 ounces would be left} \quad}$

Name _____

85 DAILY CUMULATIVE REVIEW

Write the answer.

          123 R3
1. 5)618

2.   5.069
     + 2.92
       7.989

3.   0.6
     × 0.1
       0.06

4.   53
     – 8.68
       44.32

          6.3
5. 0.6)3.78

6.   4.1
     ×   8
       32.8

7. 6768 ÷ 8

     846

8. 75 × 308

     23,100

9. 0.06 ÷ 0.15

     0.4

**List each group of numbers from least to greatest.
Then find the range, mean, median, and mode.**

10. 71, 86, 92, 100, 86 _____ 71, 86, 86, 92, 100;

     range: 29; mean: 87; median: 86; mode: 86

11. $335, $907, $582, $356 _____ $335, $356, $582, $907;

     range: $572; mean: $545; median: $469; mode: none

Solve.

12. After the softball game, Mrs. Pierce
    bought frozen juice bars for her son
    Tony and 5 of his friends. The bars
    cost $0.79 apiece. How much did she
    spend in all? $4.74

Name _____

Divide. Round the quotient to the given place.

1. hundredths   60.12 ÷ 7   _____8.59_____

2. thousandths   11.26 ÷ 3   _____3.753_____

3. tenths   2.5 ÷ 6   _____0.4_____

4. cent $8.32 ÷ 10   _____$0.83_____

5. hundredths   2 ÷ 9   _____0.22_____

6. tenths   55 ÷ 3   _____18.3_____

7. thousandths   607.1 ÷ 21   _____28.910_____

8. cent $5.89 ÷ 2   _____$2.95_____

Estimate to find the better buy. Write *a* or *b*.

9. ___a___   **a.** 5 boxes of tissue for $6.00
                  b. tissues: $1.39 per box

10. ___b___   **a.** 6 cans of tuna for $3.99
                   b. tuna: $0.59 per can

11. ___a___   **a.** 8 ounces of peanuts for $1.49
                   b. peanuts: $0.29 per ounce

12. ___b___   **a.** 4 pens for $2.89
                   b. pens: $0.69 each

87 DAILY CUMULATIVE REVIEW

Use the information in the chart help you construct a circle graph.

1. Complete the chart by finding the angle measurement of each club.

Rolling Hills School Clubs		
Club	Number of Members	Angle Measure
Photography	10	100°
Drama	8	80°
Fitness	7	70°
Library	5	50°
Chess	6	60°

2. Construct a circle graph on a separate sheet of paper. Use a compass and a protractor.

3. What is the sum of the angle measures for the circle graph?   360°

4. How did you decide the number of sections to use for the circle graph?

There is one section for each club.

5. How did you find the number of degrees per student?

Answers may vary. Some may divide 360° by 36.

88 DAILY CUMULATIVE REVIEW

Write the answer.

1. 2.977
    + 1.9
    _____
    4.877

2. 1.94
    × 12
    _____
    23.28

3. 19.7
    − 7.857
    _____
    11.843

4. 180 R2
    5)902

5. 496
    × 100
    _____
    49,600

6. 3.65
    0.523
    + 1.396
    _____
    5.569

7. 1.76 ÷ 0.22
    _____
    8

8. 46 × 0.39
    _____
    17.94

9. 758.4 ÷ 12
    _____
    63.2

Use your protractor to measure each angle.
Compare each pair of angles. Write *true* or *false*.

10. ∠ABC ≅ ∠ABF ___true___

11. ∠ABG ≅ ∠GBF ___false___

12. ∠DBE ≅ ∠ABG ___true___

13. ∠FBG ≅ ∠CBE ___false___

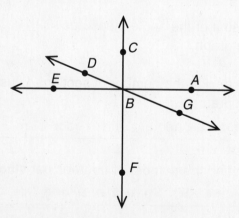

Name _____

89 ▸ DAILY CUMULATIVE REVIEW

Estimate the answer. Answers may vary. Ranges are given.

1. 507 ÷ 8   _60–65_

2. 4 × 85   _320–360_

3. 99 × 26   _2600–3000_

4. 919 ÷ 62   _10–20_

5. 8695 ÷ 24   _300–400_

6. 6362 ÷ 5   _1000–2000_

7. 38 × 287   _12,000_

8. 8 × 590   _4800_

9. 1855 ÷ 9   _180–200_

10. 3246 ÷ 37   _80–100_

Write the prime factorization of each number. If a number is already prime, write the word *prime*.
Order of listings may vary.

11. 222   _2 × 3 × 37_

12. 89   _prime_

13. 78   _2 × 3 × 13_

14. 105   _3 × 5 × 7_

15. 286   _2 × 11 × 13_

16. 37   _prime_

Solve.

17. Trisha wants to buy socks that cost $1.59 a pair. Her friend Cora says that the socks priced at 3 pairs for $4.50 are a better buy. Is Cora correct?   _yes_

Name _____

Write the answer. Use mental math.

1. $50 + 22$ _____72_____
2. $81 - 39$ _____42_____

3. $63 - 19$ _____44_____
4. $74 + 15$ _____89_____

5. $600 + 440$ _____1040_____
6. $4300 - 2800$ _____1500_____

Solve. You will need a compass and a ruler.

7. Draw a line segment $1\frac{15}{16}$ inches long. Using your compass to make congruent line segments and the corner of a sheet of paper to draw right angles, draw a square with sides that are $1\frac{15}{16}$ inches long.

   Check students' drawings.

8. Using only a compass and the corners of a sheet of paper, draw a square with sides twice as long as the square you made in exercise 7. Do this on a separate sheet of paper.

   Check students' drawings.

91 DAILY CUMULATIVE REVIEW

Write the answer.

1.
$846.36
  63.20
+ 559.84
$1469.40

2.
  600
− 2.8
 597.2

3.
  1.43
  5.90
+ 4.27
 11.60

4.
  212
× 51
10,812

5.
0.6
5) 3

6.
  783
× 134
104,922

7. 3 ÷ 12

0.25

8. $5.68 ÷ 8

$0.71

9. 1.8 ÷ 36

0.05

Write the least common multiple (LCM) and the greatest common factor (GCF) for each pair of numbers.

10. 7 and 14

LCM: 14

GCF: 7

11. 2 and 9

LCM: 18

GCF: 1

12. 25 and 60

LCM: 300

GCF: 5

Solve.

13. Jaime works 3 hours each day after school. He is paid $4.25 per hour. How much does he earn in 2 weeks?

$127.50

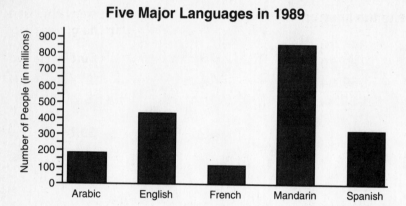

Five Major Languages in 1989

Answer each question. Use the graph.

1. Which language is spoken by more than 800 million people?

   Mandarin

2. Which language is spoken by almost 200 million people?

   Arabic

3. About how many people speak English?

   about 450 million people

4. About how many people speak Spanish?

   about 350 million people

5. Which languages are spoken by more than 200 million people?

   English, Spanish, Mandarin

Name _____

93 DAILY CUMULATIVE REVIEW

Estimate the quotient.

Answers may vary.
Accept quotients within the given range.

$0.50–$0.60
1. 4)$2.10

$60.00–$70.00
2. 5)$302.47

$0.60–$0.70
3. 7)$4.45

$0.20–$0.30
4. 3)$0.85

$1.00–$2.00
5. 6)$10.68

$9.00–$10.00
6. 9)$86.60

7. $9.21 ÷ 7

8. $16.35 ÷ 3

9. $2804 ÷ 5

$1.00–$2.00

$5.00–$6.00

$500–$600

Use a millimeter ruler to measure the sides of each triangle. Write the perimeter of each triangle in millimeters.

10. △ HJK _____155 mm_____

11. △ JLM _____78 mm_____

12. △ LHN _____78 mm_____

13. △ LMN _____78 mm_____

14. △ MNK _____78 mm_____

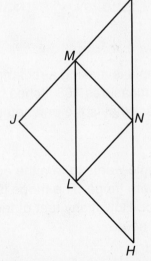

Accept all reasonable measurements close to suggested measures. Answers may vary.

94 DAILY CUMULATIVE REVIEW

Write the answer.

1. $8.52
   × 14
   119.28

2. 1.19
   $3\overline{)3.57}$

3. 80
   $50\overline{)4000}$

4. $17.99
   − 5.01
   $12.98

5. 0.34
   × 10
   3.4

6. 0.79
   $15\overline{)11.85}$

7. 8.6 + 19 + 0.7
   28.3

8. 100.2 − 35.81
   64.39

9. 803.1 − 267.5
   535.6

Solve.

10. 92 g = __0.092__ kg

11. 63 m = __6300__ cm

12. 0.8 L = __800__ mL

13. 25 mm = __2.5__ cm

Solve.

14. Mrs. Stimple is making a rectangular quilt that measures 108 inches by 80 inches. What is the perimeter of the quilt?

    376 inches

15. Mrs. Stimple wants to trim the edge of the quilt with fringe. The fringe is sold by the foot. How many feet of trim does she need?

    31.33 feet;
    she may buy 32 feet to
    be sure she has enough

95 DAILY CUMULATIVE REVIEW

Write the product or quotient. Use mental math when you can.

$$\begin{array}{r} 400 \\ 1.\ 20\overline{)8000} \end{array}$$

$$\begin{array}{r} 20 \\ 2.\ 30\overline{)600} \end{array}$$

$$\begin{array}{r} 111 \\ 3.\ 5\overline{)555} \end{array}$$

4. 102×5 ___510___

5. 8×21 ___168___

6. $14,000 \div 70$ ___200___

7. $2500 \div 10$ ___250___

8. 4×54 ___216___

9. 7×21 ___147___

Find the circumference. You may use a calculator.

10.

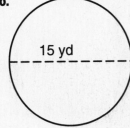

15 yd

___47.1 yd___

11.

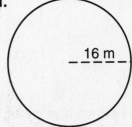

16 m

___100.48 m___

12.

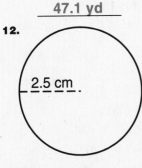

2.5 cm

___15.7 cm___

13.

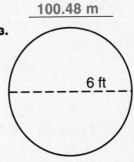

6 ft

___18.84 ft___

96 ▸ DAILY CUMULATIVE REVIEW

Classify each angle as *acute, right, obtuse*, or *straight*.

1.

∠ DEF __acute__

2.

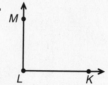

∠ MLK __right__

3.

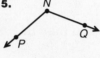

∠ DRL __straight__

4.

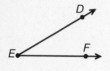

∠ BDF __obtuse__

5.

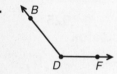

∠ PNQ __obtuse__

6.

∠ STV __acute__

Solve each problem. Write whether you used a calculator or pencil and paper. **Methods will vary.**

7. Ahmad has 400 cassette tapes. Each of his new tape racks holds 15 tapes. If he puts all his tapes in the racks, how many tapes will there be in the rack that is not full?

10 tapes

8. In 1987, United States fresh fruit consumption averaged 96.9 pounds per person per year. About how many pounds of fruit did each person eat in one week?

1.9 pounds

97 DAILY CUMULATIVE REVIEW

Write the answer.

1. $80\overline{)744}$ 9 R24

2. $1.6\overline{)0.8}$ 0.5

3. $92\overline{)4416}$ 48

4. 185
   × 158
   ‾‾‾‾‾
   29,230

5. 0.18
   ×   9
   ‾‾‾‾‾
   1.62

6. 4.64
   × 200
   ‾‾‾‾‾
   928

7. 1.872 + 3.037

   4.909

8. 5985 − 4706

   1279

9. 748.02 + 3.905

   751.925

Write the value.

10. 2 ÷ 2 + 10 _____ 11

11. (9 − 6) × 8 _____ 24

12. 7(1 + 2) ÷ 3 _____ 7

13. (5 + 5) × (5 − 4) _____ 10

Use a working-backward strategy to solve the problem.

14. So far this year, Emily's math test scores are 90, 82, 86, and 93. In order to receive an A, Emily needs an average of at least 90. There will be one more test before the end of the marking period. What is the lowest score she can get on that test to qualify for an A?

   _____ 99

Name _____

Identify each quadrilateral.

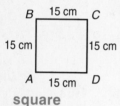

1.

B — 15 cm — C

15 cm · 15 cm

A — 15 cm — D

<u>square</u>

2.

H — 6 cm — J

3 cm / 3 cm

G — 6 cm — K

<u>parallelogram</u>

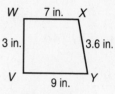

3.

W — 7 in. — X

3 in. · 3.6 in.

V — 9 in. — Y

<u>trapezoid</u>

Write an equivalent fraction.

4. $\frac{1}{2} = \frac{\boxed{4}}{8}$

5. $\frac{3}{12} = \frac{6}{\boxed{24}}$

6. $\frac{1}{\boxed{8}} = \frac{2}{16}$

7. $\frac{\boxed{3}}{6} = \frac{6}{12}$

8. $\frac{5}{8} = \frac{\boxed{15}}{24}$

9. $\frac{8}{\boxed{20}} = \frac{40}{100}$

10. $\frac{\boxed{2}}{9} = \frac{6}{27}$

11. $\frac{3}{10} = \frac{15}{\boxed{50}}$

12. $\frac{3}{5} = \frac{15}{\boxed{25}}$

Read the problem. Then make notes, make a table, or use other strategies to solve.

13. Nina is in the flag and banner corps. The corps practices for $1\frac{1}{2}$ hours after school. If practice begins at 2:45 P.M. and it takes Nina 20 minutes to get home after practice, at what time does she get home?

<u>4:35 P.M.</u>

Name _____

99 DAILY CUMULATIVE REVIEW

Write the product. Use mental math.

1. 60 × 80 ___4800___

2. 25 × 10 ___250___

3. 7 × 5 × 4 ___140___

4. 80 × 600 ___48,000___

5. 71 × 100 ___7100___

6. 4 × 300 ___1200___

7. 80 × 80 ___6400___

8. 4 × 25 × 10 ___1000___

Mrs. Emerson uses a line-plot to show the scores on the last chemistry exam. These are the test scores: 65, 70, 85, 90, 90, 100, 90, 80, 80, 85, 70, 75.

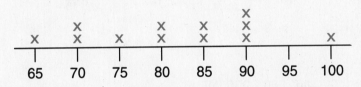

Use the test score data to complete exercises 9 and 10.

9. Complete the line-plot.

10. According to your line-plot, how many scores were less than 90?   ___8 scores___

Name _____

Write the answer. Use mental math.

1. 53 ÷ 10   _____5.3_____

2. 47 × 100   _____4700_____

3. 5.07 ÷ 100   _____0.0507_____

4. 110 ÷ 10   _____11_____

5. 21.4 × 1000   _____21,400_____

6. 353 × 100   _____35,300_____

7. 269 ÷ 1000   _____0.269_____

8. 4.356 × 10   _____43.56_____

Write <, >, or = .

9. $\frac{4}{10}$ ⊜ $\frac{2}{5}$

10. $5\frac{1}{4}$ ⊙> $4\frac{3}{4}$

11. $\frac{7}{9}$ ⊙> $\frac{2}{3}$

12. $\frac{7}{15}$ ⊙< $\frac{7}{10}$

13. $\frac{8}{12}$ ⊙> $\frac{2}{6}$

14. $6\frac{1}{3}$ ⊜ $6\frac{5}{15}$

Solve.

15. There is a circular fish pond with a diameter of 4 meters in Mrs. Mehta's back yard. She wants to put a fence around the pond's circumference before her granddaughter comes to visit. To the nearest tenth of a meter, how much fencing does she need?   _____12.6 meters_____

16. The posts that hold up the fence need to be set no further than 0.75 meter apart. How many posts should Mrs. Mehta buy?   _____17 posts_____

DAILY CUMULATIVE REVIEW

Write the answer.

1. $\begin{array}{r} 551 \\ \times\ 69 \\ \hline 38{,}019 \end{array}$

2. $\begin{array}{r} 18.357 \\ +\ 12.0833 \\ \hline 30.4403 \end{array}$

3. $\begin{array}{r} 13\ R31 \\ 67\overline{)\,902} \end{array}$

4. $\begin{array}{r} 71.08 \\ -\ 48.617 \\ \hline 22.463 \end{array}$

5. $\begin{array}{r} 2468\ ft \\ 4\overline{)\,9872\ ft} \end{array}$

6. $\begin{array}{r} \$40.67 \\ 13.86 \\ +\ 8.73 \\ \hline 63.26 \end{array}$

7. $0.29 - 0.14$ ___0.15___

8. 133×700 ___93,100___

9. 27.02×33 ___891.66___

Use your protractor to measure each angle.
Extending the lines of the figure may make
measuring angles easier.

10. ∠RST ___60°___

11. ∠NMP ___60°___

12. ∠TSV ___120°___

13. ∠XWS ___135°___

14. ∠RSW ___45°___

15. ∠TSU ___75°___

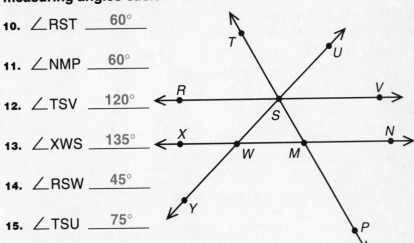

Name _____

Write the answer in simplest form.

1. $\frac{1}{8} + \frac{5}{8}$ _____ $\frac{3}{4}$

2. $\frac{4}{9} + \frac{3}{9}$ _____ $\frac{7}{9}$

3. $\frac{18}{12} - \frac{4}{12}$ _____ $1\frac{1}{6}$

4. $\frac{11}{10} - \frac{3}{10}$ _____ $\frac{4}{5}$

5. $\frac{9}{16} + \frac{2}{16}$ _____ $\frac{11}{16}$

6. $\frac{3}{4} + \frac{3}{4}$ _____ $1\frac{1}{2}$

7. $\frac{42}{100} - \frac{15}{100}$ _____ $\frac{27}{100}$

8. $\frac{7}{15} - \frac{2}{15}$ _____ $\frac{1}{3}$

Write the equivalent measure. Use the table of measures in the Data Book section of your math book.

9. 3 tons = ___6000___ lb

10. 80 fl oz = ___10___ c

11. 84 in. = ___7___ ft

12. 16 pt = ___2___ gal

13. 48 ft = ___16___ yd

14. 7 qt = ___28___ c

15. 7 gal = ___28___ qt

16. 9 yd = ___324___ in.

Solve.

17. Sergei bought a used stereo system and 25 cassettes from a friend. He paid $75 for the stereo system and $1.50 apiece for the cassettes. How much did he pay in all?

___$112.50___

Divide. Round the quotient to the given place.

1. tenths $34.21 \div 3$ _11.4_

2. hundredths $84.98 \div 5$ _17.00_

3. cent $\$83.78 \div 25$ _\$3.35_

4. thousandths $6.95 \div 13$ _0.535_

5. hundredths $625 \div 7$ _89.29_

6. cent $\$4.90 \div 6$ _\$0.82_

7. tenths $534.5 \div 4$ _133.6_

8. thousandths $13 \div 7$ _1.857_

Write in simplest form.

9. $\frac{14}{21}$ _$\frac{2}{3}$_   10. $\frac{6}{12}$ _$\frac{1}{2}$_   11. $\frac{7}{28}$ _$\frac{1}{4}$_

12. $\frac{27}{5}$ _$5\frac{2}{5}$_   13. $\frac{7}{3}$ _$2\frac{1}{3}$_   14. $\frac{16}{30}$ _$\frac{8}{15}$_

15. $\frac{9}{12}$ _$\frac{3}{4}$_   16. $\frac{11}{2}$ _$5\frac{1}{2}$_   17. $\frac{75}{100}$ _$\frac{3}{4}$_

Solve.

18. Melissa and Marco are presenting a science project together. Melissa spent $1\frac{1}{2}$ hours making graphs and charts. Marco spent $2\frac{3}{4}$ hours writing up their experiments. How much time in all did they spend preparing their presentation?   _$4\frac{1}{4}$ hours_

Name _____

Write the answer.

1. $1.9)\overline{5.7}$ → 3

2. $\begin{array}{r} 1.21 \\ \times\ \ 0.4 \\ \hline 0.484 \end{array}$

3. $\begin{array}{r} 84.018 \\ -\ \ 9.301 \\ \hline 74.717 \end{array}$

4. $\begin{array}{r} \$265.55 \\ +\ \ 147.95 \\ \hline \$413.50 \end{array}$

5. $7)\overline{59.85}$ → 8.55

6. $\begin{array}{r} 828 \\ \times\ \ 4.4 \\ \hline 3643.2 \end{array}$

7. $91 - 62.4$

28.6

8. $14.08 + 16.105$

30.185

9. $72 + 8.4 + 13.02$

93.42

Write each mixed number as a fraction.

10. $3\frac{4}{5}$ ___ $\frac{19}{5}$

11. $2\frac{7}{10}$ ___ $\frac{27}{10}$

12. $5\frac{2}{7}$ ___ $\frac{37}{7}$

13. $4\frac{1}{6}$ ___ $\frac{25}{6}$

14. $9\frac{1}{4}$ ___ $\frac{37}{4}$

15. $9\frac{2}{3}$ ___ $\frac{29}{3}$

16. $2\frac{3}{5}$ ___ $\frac{13}{5}$

17. $5\frac{1}{8}$ ___ $\frac{41}{8}$

18. $8\frac{9}{10}$ ___ $\frac{89}{10}$

Solve.

19. One cup of apple juice has 120 Calories. How many Calories are there in one fluid ounce of apple juice?

15 Calories

Name _____

Estimate the sum or difference. **Answers may vary.**

1. $\frac{5}{6} + \frac{7}{8}$ _____2_____

2. $3\frac{1}{5} - 1\frac{3}{4}$ _____1_____

3. $\frac{11}{12} + \frac{5}{6} + \frac{7}{10}$ _____$2\frac{1}{2}$_____

4. $7\frac{1}{8} - \frac{2}{5}$ _____7_____

5. $6\frac{11}{15} - \frac{5}{6}$ _____6_____

6. $\frac{3}{16} + \frac{3}{4} + \frac{3}{7}$ _____$1\frac{1}{2}$_____

7. $\frac{4}{9} + 5\frac{5}{8} + 1\frac{1}{3}$ _____$7\frac{1}{2}$_____

8. $9\frac{2}{3} - 4\frac{7}{12}$ _____5_____

Round to the underlined place.

9. 7,100,659 _7,000,000_

10. 54,706 _55,000_

11. 354,622 _400,000_

12. 8593 _8590_

13. 281,356 _281,400_

14. 457,903 _500,000_

15. 605,291 _610,000_

16. 2635 _2600_

Solve.

17. The public libraries in Albuquerque, New Mexico have an annual circulation of about 2,250,000 books. In Pittsburgh, Pennsylvania the public libraries have an annual circulation of about 2,800,000 books. Which city's libraries have the greater annual circulation?

_____**Pittsburgh, Pennsylvania**_____

106 DAILY CUMULATIVE REVIEW

Write the answer. Use mental math.

1. 0.004×10 ___0.04___

2. 3.2×1000 ___3200___

3. $\$6.59 \times 100$ ___$659___

4. $14.3 \times 10 =$ ___143___

5. 0.0016×1000 ___1.6___

6. 2.084×100 ___208.4___

Solve.

7. $\$0.19 \cdot a = \$19.00$

___$a = 100$___

8. $n \cdot 10 = 260$

___$n = 26$___

Find the circumference. You may use a calculator. Use 3.14 for π.

9.

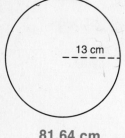

13 cm

___81.64 cm___

10.

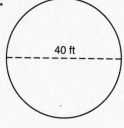

40 ft

___125.6 ft___

11.

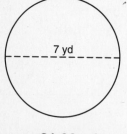

7 yd

___21.98 yd___

12.

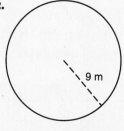

9 m

___56.52 m___

Use mental math to solve.

1. $\frac{1}{2} + 1\frac{1}{4}$ ___$1\frac{3}{4}$___

2. $\frac{3}{4} + \frac{3}{4}$ ___$1\frac{1}{2}$___

3. $5\frac{1}{2} + 1\frac{1}{4}$ ___$6\frac{3}{4}$___

4. $3\frac{3}{4} + 9\frac{3}{4}$ ___$13\frac{1}{2}$___

5. $1 - \frac{7}{15}$ ___$\frac{8}{15}$___

6. $1 - \frac{7}{12}$ ___$\frac{5}{12}$___

7. $\frac{1}{4} + \frac{3}{4} + 2\frac{1}{2}$ ___$3\frac{1}{2}$___

8. $7\frac{1}{2} + \frac{1}{4} + 5\frac{1}{4}$ ___13___

Write an equivalent fraction.

9. $\frac{5}{6} = \frac{\boxed{15}}{18}$

10. $\frac{11}{12} = \frac{\boxed{22}}{24}$

11. $\frac{4}{5} = \frac{\boxed{16}}{20}$

12. $\frac{3}{4} = \frac{\boxed{12}}{16}$

13. $\frac{5}{8} = \frac{15}{\boxed{24}}$

14. $\frac{3}{9} = \frac{\boxed{12}}{36}$

15. $\frac{1}{3} = \frac{\boxed{6}}{18}$

16. $\frac{7}{8} = \frac{35}{\boxed{40}}$

17. $\frac{2}{3} = \frac{8}{\boxed{12}}$

Solve.

18. During recess, $\frac{1}{4}$ of Mrs. Orosco's class played dodge ball; $\frac{1}{3}$ played tether ball; $\frac{1}{6}$ played on the rope climb; and the remaining 6 students jumped rope. How many students are in Mrs. Orosco's class?

24 students

Name _____

Write the answer.

1.
```
    1.81
  ×    9
  16.29
```

2.
```
    3772
  + 1682
    5454
```

3.
```
    1190
  −  563
     627
```

4.
```
      67 R6
  13 )877
```

5.
```
     269
  ×   87
  23,403
```

6.
```
   $90.18
  −  9.02
    81.16
```

7. $0.242 \div 10$

0.0242

8. 7.82×10

78.2

9. 4.87×0.1

0.487

Look at rectangle *ABCD* and its two diagonals.

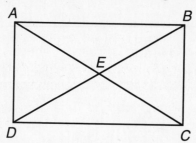

10. Name two acute angles in the figure.

Answers may vary but may include ∠AED, ∠BEC.

11. Name two right angles in the figure.

Answers may vary but may include ∠DAB, ∠BCD.

12. Name two obtuse angles in the figure.

∠AEB, ∠CED.

13. Name two straight angles in the figure.

∠AEC, ∠DEB.

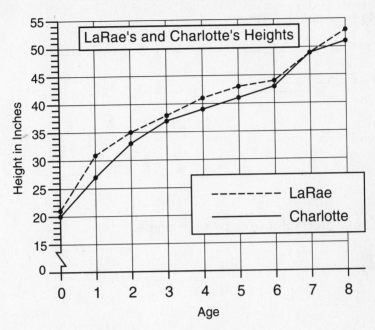

Write each answer. Use the graph above.

1. Which girl was almost always taller ?

   LaRae

2. At what age were the two girls the same height?

   7 years old

3. How tall was LaRae when she was 5 years old?

   43 inches

4. How tall was Charlotte when she was 3 years old?

   37 inches

5. At what ages was LaRae at least 2 inches taller than Charlotte?

   1 year old; 2 years old; 4 years old; 5 years old; 8 years old

Name _____

DAILY CUMULATIVE REVIEW

....

Write in simplest form.

1. $\frac{1}{2} + \frac{7}{8}$ ___$1\frac{3}{8}$___

2. $\frac{2}{3} - \frac{4}{9}$ ___$\frac{2}{9}$___

3. $2\frac{4}{5} - \frac{3}{10}$ ___$2\frac{1}{2}$___

4. $8\frac{5}{12} + 4\frac{1}{3}$ ___$12\frac{3}{4}$___

5. $\frac{11}{12} + \frac{1}{6}$ ___$1\frac{1}{12}$___

6. $2\frac{3}{4} - \frac{5}{8}$ ___$2\frac{1}{8}$___

7. $6\frac{3}{10} + 4\frac{1}{2}$ ___$10\frac{4}{5}$___

8. $5\frac{5}{6} - 1\frac{1}{2}$ ___$4\frac{1}{3}$___

Use your protractor to draw each angle.

Check students' drawings.

9. $125°$

10. $35°$

11. $170°$

Solve.

12. In 1975, the average starting salary for an engineer was $12,744. In 1988, the average starting salary was $29,856. How much greater was the starting salary in 1988? ___$17,112___

Name _____

111 DAILY CUMULATIVE REVIEW

Add or subtract. Use the table of measures in the Data Book.

Some possible answers are shown.

1. 6 ft 2 in. + 4 in.

$6\frac{1}{2}$ ft or 6 ft 6 in.

2. 7 lb – 3 lb 8 oz

$3\frac{1}{2}$ lb or 3 lb 8 oz

3. 1 gal 2 pt + 2 gal 4 pt

3 gal 6 pt, 3 gal 3 qt, or $3\frac{3}{4}$ gal

4. 12 h 15 min – 4 h 45 min

7 h 30 min or $7\frac{1}{2}$ h

5. 8 lb 4 oz – 2 lb 8 oz

5 lb 12 oz or $5\frac{3}{4}$ lb

6. 15 ft 9 in. + 6 ft 9 in.

22 ft 6 in. or $22\frac{1}{2}$ ft

7. 5 h 15 min + 2 h 15 min

7 h 30 min or $7\frac{1}{2}$ h

8. 10 gal 6 pt – 5 gal 2 pt

5 gal 4 pt, 5 gal 2 qt, or $5\frac{1}{2}$ gal

Write a multiplication or division expression for each situation. Tell what the variable stands for.

Accept any reasonable expression.

9. Cai bought a new collar for each of her 3 cats. The amount she spent =

$3 \cdot c$; c is the cost of a collar

10. Mark passed out all 60 of his marbles for a game. Each player got the same number of marbles. The number of marbles each player received =

$60 \div p$; p is the number of players

Name _____

Write the answer.

1.
```
   72 R4
7) 508
```

2.
```
   1.5
 × 0.4
   0.6
```

3.
```
   $5.42
4) $21.68
```

4.
```
   0.74
 ×    9
   6.66
```

5.
```
   1.31
6) 7.86
```

6.
```
   $745
 ×    4
  $2980
```

7. 8.8 ÷ 0.2

44

8. 90 × 91

8190

9. 4.7 × 8.6

40.42

Write whether each fraction is close to 0, $\frac{1}{2}$, or 1.

10. $\frac{6}{16}$ _____ $\frac{1}{2}$

11. $\frac{11}{18}$ _____ $\frac{1}{2}$

12. $\frac{3}{20}$ _____ 0

13. $\frac{3}{7}$ _____ $\frac{1}{2}$

14. $\frac{81}{100}$ _____ 1

15. $\frac{940}{1000}$ _____ 1

Solve the problem. Estimate if it helps you.

16. A 48-ounce can of pineapple juice costs $1.59.
A quart jar of pineapple juice costs $1.29. Which
container costs less per ounce?

the 48-ounce can

Name _____

Write the answer in simplest form.

1. $4\frac{2}{5}$
$+ 3\frac{1}{3}$
$\overline{7\frac{11}{15}}$

2. $6\frac{1}{4}$
$- 1\frac{2}{3}$
$\overline{4\frac{7}{12}}$

3. $\frac{1}{6}$
$+ \frac{7}{9}$
$\overline{\frac{17}{18}}$

4. $7\frac{1}{2}$
$- 4\frac{7}{8}$
$\overline{2\frac{5}{8}}$

5. $3\frac{2}{5}$
$- \frac{1}{4}$
$\overline{3\frac{3}{20}}$

6. $13\frac{1}{6}$
$- 7\frac{3}{4}$
$\overline{5\frac{5}{12}}$

7. $6\frac{7}{10} + 4\frac{3}{5} + \frac{1}{2}$
$11\frac{4}{5}$

8. $\frac{2}{7} + 7\frac{5}{14} + 1\frac{1}{2}$
$9\frac{1}{7}$

Solve. Write whether you used a calculator or mental math. Solution methods may vary; *mm* is mental math; *c* is calculator

9. 69×152 10,488; c

10. $200 \div 5$ 40; mm

11. $3005 - 2000$ 1005; mm

12. $565 + 63 + 115$ 743; c

13. $198 + 798$ 996; mm

14. 19×50 950; mm

15. Last year Bessie saved $10 each week for 48 weeks. How much did she save in all?

$480; mm

Name _____

DAILY CUMULATIVE REVIEW

Estimate the answer.   Answers may vary. Sample answers are given.

1. $1917 \div 8$ _200–300_

2. 62×18 _1200_

3. $7 \times \$0.44$ _$2.80–$3.50_

4. $1222 \div 6$ _200_

5. $2310 \div 90$ _20–30_

6. $9160 \div 53$ _100–200_

7. $5 \times \$8.29$ _$40–$45_

8. 24×459 _8000–10,000_

Solve the equations.

9. $b + 6 = 15$
   $$b = 9$$

10. $25 = t - 6$
    $$t = 31$$

11. $17 + h = 22$
    $$h = 5$$

12. $x - 4 = 50$
    $$x = 54$$

Solve.

13. Alvin keeps track of how long he practices the piano each day. Last week he recorded these times: 48 minutes, 35 minutes, 1 hour, $\frac{1}{2}$ hour, and 65 minutes. To the nearest minute, what was his average daily practice time?

    48 minutes

Name _____

Write the answer in simplest form.

1. $\frac{14}{16} - \frac{8}{16}$ _____ $\frac{3}{8}$

2. $\frac{3}{4} + \frac{3}{4}$ _____ $1\frac{1}{2}$

3. $\frac{4}{5} + \frac{3}{5}$ _____ $1\frac{2}{5}$

4. $\frac{10}{8} - \frac{7}{8}$ _____ $\frac{3}{8}$

5. $\frac{9}{12} + \frac{5}{12}$ _____ $1\frac{1}{6}$

6. $\frac{95}{100} - \frac{70}{100}$ _____ $\frac{1}{4}$

7. $\frac{9}{6} - \frac{1}{6}$ _____ $1\frac{1}{3}$

8. $\frac{6}{15} + \frac{10}{15}$ _____ $1\frac{1}{15}$

Complete. Write <, >, or = .

9. 5.1 L $>$ 510 mL

10. 60 cm $=$ 600 mm

11. 0.78 m $<$ 85 cm

12. 2900 g $>$ 0.29 kg

13. 12 mL $<$ 0.05 L

14. 0.286 kg $=$ 286 g

Solve.

15. Karina is participating in a dairy goat project with her 4-H club. She milks her goat twice a day and gets 4 pints of milk each time. How many ounces of milk does the goat give each day?

128 ounces

16. Last year, Karina's family had an income of $28,365. Out of this, they paid $7091 in taxes. How much money was left after taxes?

$21,274

17. What percent of their income were the taxes?

25%

Name _____

 116 DAILY CUMULATIVE REVIEW

Write the answer.

1. $27 \div 0.9$ _____30_____

2. 41.3×6 _____247.8_____

3. $7239 \div 18$ _____402 R3_____

4. 9.1×0.5 _____4.55_____

5. $\$107.94 \div 21$ _____\$5.14_____

6. 802.3×0.05 _____40.115_____

7. $131 \div 12$ _____10 R11_____

8. 70.6×0.8 _____56.48_____

9. $402 \div 17$ _____23 R11_____

10. 0.06×87 _____5.22_____

Use the grid to solve. Use the clues to cross out choices.

11. Connie, Latisha, Lisa, and Peggy have different favorite zoo animals. One girl likes elephants, another likes tigers, one likes koala bears, and one likes penguins. Connie's favorite animal is larger than a penguin. Lisa likes the biggest animal. Peggy's favorite animal lives in trees. Name each person's favorite.

	Connie	Latisha	Lisa	Peggy
elephants				
koala bears				
penguins				
tigers				

Favorite Animals

Connie _____tigers_____

Latisha _____penguins_____

Lisa _____elephants_____

Peggy _____Koala bears_____

Name _____

Write the answer.

1.
$$
\begin{array}{r}
\$56.95 \\
72.29 \\
+\ 16.76 \\
\hline
\$146.00
\end{array}
$$

2.
$$
\begin{array}{r}
3.42 \\
0.52 \\
+\ 3.19 \\
\hline
7.13
\end{array}
$$

3.
$$
\begin{array}{r}
2772 \\
-\ 1999 \\
\hline
773
\end{array}
$$

Write the answer. Use the graph.

Survey of High School
Students' Favorite Music

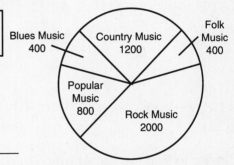

4. How many students
   were in the survey?

   4800 students

5. How many students like popular music best? Is
   this more or less than $\frac{1}{4}$ of all the students who
   were surveyed?

   800 students; less than $\frac{1}{4}$ of the students surveyed

6. What two types of music together are preferred by
   half of the students surveyed? How many
   students is that?

   folk and rock, or blues and rock; 2400 students

7. According to the survey, what types of music are
   less popular than country music?

   popular, folk, and blues

Name _____

 DAILY CUMULATIVE REVIEW ·······················

Write the answer in simplest form.

1. $\frac{9}{16}$
    $+\frac{3}{8}$
    $\overline{\frac{15}{16}}$

2. $5\frac{1}{4}$
    $+3\frac{3}{5}$
    $\overline{8\frac{17}{20}}$

3. $6\frac{7}{10}$
    $+1\frac{2}{3}$
    $\overline{8\frac{11}{30}}$

4. $\frac{7}{8}$
    $-\frac{1}{6}$
    $\overline{\frac{17}{24}}$

5. $4\frac{1}{5}$
    $-2\frac{1}{3}$
    $\overline{1\frac{13}{15}}$

6. $9\frac{2}{9}$
    $-6\frac{1}{2}$
    $\overline{2\frac{13}{18}}$

7. $\frac{1}{5} \times \frac{5}{6}$ ____$\frac{1}{6}$____

8. $\frac{2}{3} \times \frac{7}{8}$ ____$\frac{7}{12}$____

Estimate to find the better buy. Write *a* or *b*.

9. ___b___ a. 3 pairs of sunglasses for $10.00
            b. sunglasses: $2.99 per pair

10. ___a___ a. 5 notebooks for $5.50
             b. notebooks: $1.19 each

11. ___a___ a. 3 pounds of pears for $1.99
             b. pears: $0.69 a pound

12. ___b___ a. 10 cans of dog food for $8.00
             b. dog food: $0.75 a can

13. ___b___ a. 6 toothbrushes for $15.00
             b. toothbrushes: $2.39 each

14. ___a___ a. 4 pair of socks for $5.79
             b. socks: $1.49 per pair

Name _____

 DAILY CUMULATIVE REVIEW ....

Write the answer in simplest form.

1. $3\frac{1}{3}$
$+\ 2\frac{2}{3}$
_____
6

2. 1.302
$+\ 0.5193$
_____
1.8213

3. $9\frac{3}{8}$
$+\ 1\frac{3}{16}$
_____
$10\frac{9}{16}$

4. $5\frac{7}{9}$
$-\ 2\frac{1}{3}$
_____
$3\frac{4}{9}$

5. $25,573$
$-\ 13,891$
_____
$11,682$

6. $4\frac{6}{7}$
$-\ 2\frac{1}{7}$
_____
$2\frac{5}{7}$

7. 90×608 _____54,720_____   **8.** $\frac{1}{4} \times 6\frac{2}{3}$ _____$1\frac{2}{3}$_____

Write each mixed number as a fraction.

9. $3\frac{5}{8}$ ___$\frac{29}{8}$___   **10.** $6\frac{1}{2}$ ___$\frac{13}{2}$___   **11.** $10\frac{2}{3}$ ___$\frac{32}{3}$___

12. $5\frac{9}{10}$ ___$\frac{59}{10}$___   **13.** $8\frac{5}{6}$ ___$\frac{53}{6}$___   **14.** $4\frac{8}{9}$ ___$\frac{44}{9}$___

Solve.

15. Mrs. Tucker plans to jog 1 mile each day during the first week. Then she plans to add $\frac{1}{4}$ mile each week to her daily distance. How far will she be jogging each day during the 8th week?

_____$2\frac{3}{4}$ miles_____

16. Mr. Tucker plans to jog 2 miles each day during the first week and then add $\frac{1}{8}$ mile each week to his daily distance. How far will he be jogging each day during the 8th week?

_____$2\frac{7}{8}$ miles_____

Name _____

 120 DAILY CUMULATIVE REVIEW
···

Divide. Round the quotient to the given place.

1. thousandths $9.61 \div 8$ 1.201

2. tenths $230 \div 3$ 76.7

3. cent $\$7.44 \div 13$ $\$0.57$

4. hundredths $8.68 \div 9$ 0.96

5. tenths $8 \div 7$ 1.1

6. hundredths $19.07 \div 65$ 0.29

7. thousandths $6.04 \div 27$ 0.224

Write each fraction or mixed number as an equivalent decimal.

8. $\frac{3}{4}$ 0.75   9. $5\frac{1}{2}$ 5.5   10. $\frac{4}{5}$ 0.8

11. $3\frac{9}{10}$ 3.9   12. $\frac{67}{100}$ 0.67   13. $9\frac{9}{20}$ 9.45

Solve.

14. Philip and 3 friends bought 2 pizzas. They each ate the same amount and they finished both pizzas. What fraction of a pizza did each boy eat? $\frac{1}{2}$ pizza

15. The 4 boys also shared $1\frac{1}{3}$ quarts of juice. If each boy drank the same amount of juice, how much did each drink? $\frac{1}{3}$ quart

121 DAILY CUMULATIVE REVIEW

Write the product in simplest form.

1. $\frac{1}{6} \times 12$ _____ 2 _____   2. $5\frac{1}{4} \times 3\frac{1}{6}$ _____ $16\frac{5}{8}$

3. $2 \times \frac{1}{5}$ _____ $\frac{2}{5}$ _____   4. $24 \times 6\frac{1}{3}$ _____ 152

5. $8\frac{2}{7} \times 3\frac{1}{2}$ _____ 29 _____   6. $\frac{2}{3}$ of 15 _____ 10

7. $10\frac{1}{3} \times \frac{1}{6}$ _____ $1\frac{13}{18}$ _____   8. $10 \times \frac{1}{8}$ _____ $1\frac{1}{4}$

Write each ratio below at least three different ways.

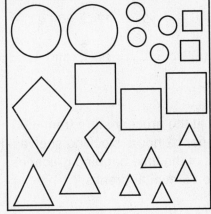

9. large circles to small circles _____ 2 to 4; 2:4; $\frac{2}{4}$

10. all triangles to all circles _____ 7 to 6; 7:6; $\frac{7}{6}$

11. small shapes to large shapes _____ 12 to 8; 12:8; $\frac{12}{8}$

12. small kites to small squares _____ 1 to 2; 1:2; $\frac{1}{2}$

13. large triangles to total shapes _____ 2 to 20; 2:20; $\frac{2}{20}$

Name _____

....

Accept all reasonable estimates. Possible estimates are given.
Estimate.

1. $\frac{1}{4}$ of 79 ____about 20____   2. $\frac{1}{7}$ of $39 ____about $5–$6____

3. $\frac{2}{5}$ of 24 ____about 9–10____   4. $\frac{3}{4}$ of 169 ____about 120____

5. $\frac{1}{6}$ of 57 ____about 10____   6. $\frac{2}{3}$ of 45 ____about 20–30____

7. $\frac{1}{8}$ of 358 ___about 40–50___   8. $\frac{3}{10}$ of $360 ___about $90–$120___

**Which of the pairs below are reciprocals? Write *yes*
or *no*.**

9. $\frac{3}{8}$ and $\frac{8}{3}$ ____yes____   10. $\frac{1}{2}$ and $\frac{5}{2}$ ____no____

11. $\frac{7}{3}$ and $\frac{3}{5}$ ____no____   12. $\frac{3}{5}$ and $\frac{5}{3}$ ____yes____

Solve.

13. Ervin worked at the grocery store from 6:00 A.M.
to noon. He spent 2 hours stocking shelves. He
spent the rest of the time bagging groceries,
except for two 15-minute breaks.

a. What fraction of the time did Ervin work
bagging groceries?

$\frac{7}{12}$ of the time

b. Did he spend more than $\frac{1}{2}$ of the time bagging
groceries?

yes

Name _____

Add or subtract. Use the table of measures in the Data Book at the back of your math textbook.
Some possible answers shown.

1. 9 ft 6 in. − 8 ft 3 in.   1 ft 3 in. or $1\frac{1}{4}$ ft

2. 8 lb 4 oz − 2 lb 12 oz   5 lb 8 oz or $5\frac{1}{2}$ lb

3. 4 h 15 min − 45 min $3\frac{1}{2}$ h or 3 h 30 min

4. 9 gal 4 pt + 1 gal 2 pt   10 gal 6 pt or $10\frac{3}{4}$ gal

5. 7 ft 3 in. + 2 ft 3 in. $9\frac{1}{2}$ ft or 9 ft 6 in.

6. 5 lb 4 oz + 3 lb 8 oz   8 lb 12 oz or $8\frac{3}{4}$ lb

List each group of numbers from least to greatest. Then find the range, mean, median, and mode.

7. 98, 194, 333, 22, 178   22, 98, 178, 194, 333;

     range: 311; mean: 165; median: 178; mode: none

8. $16, $21, $16, $9, $16, $12 $9, $12, $16, $16, $16, $21;

     range: $12; mean: $15; median: $16; mode: $16

Solve.

9. Frank has 3 cats, Sylvester, Sadie, and Molly. Sylvester weighs 11 pounds 3 ounces, Sadie weighs 8 pounds 9 ounces, and Molly weighs 7 pounds 5 ounces. How much do his cats weigh altogether?

     27 pounds 1 ounce

DAILY CUMULATIVE REVIEW

Write the quotient in simplest form.

1. $5 \div \frac{1}{4}$ _____ 20   **2.** $5\frac{1}{3} \div 1\frac{1}{9}$ _____ $4\frac{4}{5}$

3. $1\frac{2}{3} \div 4\frac{1}{6}$ _____ $\frac{2}{5}$ **4.** $\frac{4}{5} \div \frac{2}{5}$ _____ 2

5. $6 \div \frac{7}{10}$ _____ $8\frac{4}{7}$ **6.** $14\frac{2}{5} \div \frac{9}{10}$ _____ 16

7. $\frac{11}{12} \div 2\frac{3}{4}$ _____ $\frac{1}{3}$ **8.** $40 \div \frac{5}{8}$ _____ 64

Write the value.

9. $8 \div 2 - 3 + 10$ _____ 11   **10.** $(7 + 9) \div 4$ _____ 4

11. $3 + (7 \times 2) - 1$ _____ 16   **12.** $(38 - 2) \div 6 + 20$ _____ 26

Solve.

13. Mr. Ortega feeds his sheep a 50-pound bale of hay each day. How many pounds of hay does he need to feed his sheep during the months of October, November, and December? Is that more or less than 2 tons?

4600 pounds; more than 2 tons

14. Mrs. Minton wants to buy a television that is on sale for $\frac{1}{3}$ off. The regular price is $729.00. How much will she save by buying the television on sale? What is the sale price?

$243.00; $486.00

Name _____

 DAILY CUMULATIVE REVIEW

Write the answer. Use mental math.

1. 6.26 ÷ 10   _0.626_   2. 89 × 10   _890_

3. 0.16 × 100   _16_   4. 0.26 ÷ 10   _0.026_

5. 0.083 × 1000   _83_   6. 131 ÷ 1000   _0.131_

7. 3.6 ÷ 100   _0.036_   8. 590 × 100   _59,000_

Write each decimal as an equivalent fraction or mixed number. Write in simplest form.

9. 0.65 $\frac{13}{20}$ 10. 0.92 $\frac{23}{25}$ 11. 4.4 $4\frac{2}{5}$

12. 0.75 $\frac{3}{4}$ 13. 0.375 $\frac{3}{8}$ 14. 1.6 $1\frac{3}{5}$

Solve.

15. Roberto packed 3 T-shirts, 2 pairs of shorts, and 1 pair of jeans to wear while visiting his grandparents. If each T-shirt can be worn with either pair of shorts or with the jeans, how many different outfits can Roberto make?   **9 outfits**

16. Hillsview is 857 miles north of Port Marcy. Clearview is 274 miles south of Port Marcy. How far is Hillsview from Clearview?   **1131 miles**

Name _____

··

Write the answer in simplest form.

1. $5\frac{3}{10}$
    $+ \frac{1}{3}$
    _____
    $5\frac{19}{30}$

2. $7\frac{1}{12}$
    $- 3\frac{3}{4}$
    _____
    $3\frac{1}{3}$

3. $9\frac{5}{16}$
    $+ 1\frac{1}{8}$
    _____
    $10\frac{7}{16}$

4. $5\frac{1}{4} \times \frac{1}{7}$ _____ $\frac{3}{4}$

5. $9 \div \frac{3}{5}$ _____ 15

6. $\frac{1}{2} \times \frac{3}{5} \times \frac{5}{8}$ _____ $\frac{3}{16}$

7. $9\frac{3}{4} \div 7\frac{1}{2}$ _____ $1\frac{3}{10}$

Find the missing number for the pair of equal ratios.

8. $\frac{5}{9} = \frac{15}{h}$ _____ 27

9. $\frac{5}{12} = \frac{m}{24}$ _____ 10

10. $\frac{6}{2} = \frac{36}{n}$ _____ 12

11. $\frac{9}{8} = \frac{s}{64}$ _____ 72

Solve.

12. A recipe for bran muffins calls for 2
    cups of raisins to every 4 cups of
    bran. If Cynthia wants to use 6 cups
    of bran, how many cups of raisins
    should she use?   ___3 cups___

13. The bran muffin recipe to make
    36 muffins uses 4 cups of bran. How
    many muffins will it make using
    6 cups of bran?   ___54 muffins___

14. The recipe requires $\frac{1}{3}$ cup of chopped
    apples for each cup of bran. How
    many cups of chopped apples should
    Cynthia use for 6 cups of bran?   ___2 cups___

Name _____

Solve each problem mentally.

1. $\frac{2}{5}$ of 100 ___40___

2. $\frac{3}{7}$ of 35 ___15___

3. $\frac{7}{10}$ of 80 ___56___

4. $\frac{1}{6}$ of 66 ___11___

5. $\frac{1}{4}$ of 160 ___40___

6. $\frac{3}{8}$ of 240 ___90___

7. $\frac{2}{4}$ of 270 ___135___

8. $\frac{2}{9}$ of 54 ___12___

Write the least common multiple (LCM) and the greatest common factor (GCF) for each set of numbers.

9. 3, 6, and 8 _____LCM: 24; GCF: 1_____

10. 6, 16, and 24 _____LCM: 48; GCF: 2_____

11. 3, 4, and 42 _____LCM: 84; GCF: 1_____

12. 8, 16, 32 _____LCM: 32; GCF: 8_____

13. 5, 25, 30 _____LCM: 150; GCF: 5_____

14. 9, 27, 54 _____LCM: 54; GCF: 9_____

Solve.

15. Marina cut a loaf of banana bread into 10 equal slices. She and two friends ate $\frac{3}{5}$ of the loaf. How many slices did they eat? ___6 slices___

DAILY CUMULATIVE REVIEW

Write the answer. Look for ways to use mental math.

1.   91,875
       − 6,184
       ‾‾‾‾‾‾‾
         85,691

2.   32,086
       + 16,014
       ‾‾‾‾‾‾‾
         48,100

3.   257
         × 68
         ‾‾‾‾‾
         17,476

4. 88)‾1309‾   **14 R 77**

5. 3)‾75,004‾   **25,001 R1**

6.   57
         × 30
         ‾‾‾‾
         1710

7. 532 + 68 + 83 ___**683**___

8. 60 × 5 × 20 ___**6000**___

**Find the circumference. You may use a calculator.
Use 3.14 for π.**

9.

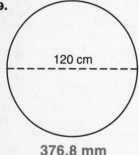

120 cm

_____**376.8 mm**_____

10.

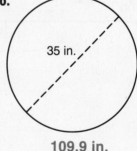

35 in.

_____**109.9 in.**_____

11.

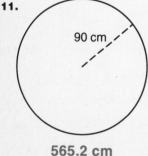

90 cm

_____**565.2 cm**_____

12.

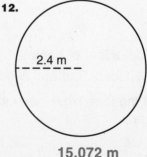

2.4 m

_____**15.072 m**_____

Name _____

Write the answer in simplest form.

1. $27 \times \frac{1}{9}$ _____ 3

2. $\frac{1}{5} \div \frac{3}{10}$ _____ $\frac{2}{3}$

3. $\frac{4}{5} \times \frac{4}{9}$ _____ $\frac{16}{45}$

4. $7 \div \frac{2}{3}$ _____ $10\frac{1}{2}$

5. $2\frac{1}{8} \times 40$ _____ 85

6. $7\frac{1}{2} \div 1\frac{1}{4}$ _____ 6

Solve. Look for ways to use mental math.

7. $12 = 36 \div n$ _____ $n = 3$

8. $40 \div p = 20$ _____ $p = 2$

9. $54 \div s = 9$ _____ $s = 6$

10. $49 = h \div 7$ _____ $h = 343$

Solve.

11. Rachel and Caleb each made a pitcher of apple juice to serve at the PTA meeting. Rachel used 1 cup of apple juice concentrate to 3 cups of water. Caleb used 1 cup of concentrate to 4 cups of water. Which pitcher of apple juice had more flavor?

Rachel's pitcher
_____

12. Fred used 5 cups of oatmeal to make 8 cups of granola. How much oatmeal should he use to make 24 cups of granola?

15 cups of oatmeal
_____

13. Allison used 3 cups of granola to make 18 cookies. How many cookies could she make with 6 cups of granola?

36 cookies
_____

Name _____

....

Estimate each sum or difference.

Accept any reasonable estimate.

1. 3.2 m + 8.66 m ___12 m___   2. $41.91 – $15.25 ___$20–$25___

3. 92 + 21 + 47 ___160___   4. 3432 – 2165 ___1000–1300___

5. 7253 – 970 ___6000___   6. 1.5 + 0.28 + 9.08 ___11___

7. 15.73 – 2.184 ___13.5–14___   8. $48.67 + $9.92 ___$58–$60___

Write the equivalent measure. Use the table of measures in the Data Book section of your math book.

9. 12 yd = ___36___ ft   10. 3 lb = ___48___ oz

11. 180 in. = ___15___ ft   12. ___11___ qt = 44 c

13. ___8000___ lb = 4 tons   14. 64 c = ___4___ gal

Solve.

15. In 1991, the salary of the governor of Louisiana was was $73,440 and the lieutenant governor's salary was $63,367. How much more was the governor paid than was the lieutenant governor?   ___$10,073___

16. That same year, the governor of California was paid a salary $120,000. How much more than the governor of Louisiana did the governor of California earn?   ___$46,560___

Name _____

Write the answer in simplest form.

1. $3\frac{2}{3}$
    $+ 6\frac{1}{4}$
    _____
    $9\frac{11}{12}$

2. $\frac{5}{7}$
    $- \frac{2}{7}$
    _____
    $\frac{3}{7}$

3. $11\frac{7}{10}$
    $+ 8\frac{3}{4}$
    _____
    $20\frac{9}{20}$

4. $18\frac{1}{2}$
    $- 5\frac{2}{5}$
    _____
    $13\frac{1}{10}$

5. $\frac{63}{100}$
    $+ \frac{26}{100}$
    _____
    $\frac{89}{100}$

6. $7\frac{1}{2}$
    $- \frac{7}{8}$
    _____
    $6\frac{5}{8}$

7. $\frac{2}{3} + \frac{4}{15}$ _____ $\frac{14}{15}$

8. $\frac{15}{16} - \frac{9}{16}$ _____ $\frac{3}{8}$

Write the letter of the proportion that matches the problem.

Jim is reading *Treasure Island*. He finds he can read 1 page in 2 minutes.

9. How many pages can Jim read in 10 minutes? _____ a

   a. $\dfrac{1 \text{ page}}{2 \text{ minutes}} = \dfrac{n \text{ pages}}{10 \text{ minutes}}$ b. $\dfrac{1 \text{ page}}{2 \text{ minutes}} = \dfrac{10 \text{ minutes}}{n \text{ pages}}$

10. How many minutes will it take him to read 20 pages? _____ b

   a. $\dfrac{1 \text{ page}}{2 \text{ minutes}} = \dfrac{n \text{ minutes}}{20 \text{ pages}}$ b. $\dfrac{1 \text{ page}}{2 \text{ minutes}} = \dfrac{20 \text{ pages}}{n \text{ minutes}}$

Name _____

 DAILY CUMULATIVE REVIEW

Write the answer.

1.
$$1.8$$
$$\times\ 0.4$$
$$\overline{0.72}$$

2.
$$0.9\overline{)2.25}$$ 2.5

3.
$$29\overline{)\$503.15}$$ $17.35

4.
$$\$367.68$$
$$200.71$$
$$+\ \ \ 96.01$$
$$\overline{\$664.40}$$

5.
$$303.22$$
$$-\ \ 91.34$$
$$\overline{211.88}$$

6.
$$0.685$$
$$5.66$$
$$+\ 9.057$$
$$\overline{15.402}$$

7. 50×3.39 _____169.5_____

8. $6 \div 24$ _____0.25_____

Use the cross–products method to check whether the ratios are equal. Write *yes* or *no*.

9. $\frac{3}{6}, \frac{6}{10}$ _____no_____

10. $\frac{5}{15}, \frac{2}{3}$ _____no_____

11. $\frac{1}{5}, \frac{4}{20}$ _____yes_____

12. $\frac{8}{10}, \frac{4}{5}$ _____yes_____

Solve.

13. Carl likes to play a word game where each player uses 9 alphabet cards. How many people can play with 36 cards?

_____4 people_____

14. Yolanda and 3 friends played a board game from 2 P.M. until 4:30 P.M. After dinner they played again for 45 minutes. How long did they play in all?

_____3 h 15 min, or $3\frac{1}{4}$ h_____

Name _____

Write the product in the simplest form. Look for ways to use mental math.

1. $\frac{4}{9}$ of 27 _____12_____   2. $\frac{5}{9} \times \frac{1}{3}$ _____$\frac{5}{27}$_____

3. $\frac{1}{8} \times 64$ _____8_____   4. $\frac{1}{2} \times \frac{1}{8}$ _____$\frac{1}{16}$_____

5. $\frac{5}{12} \times \frac{2}{5}$ _____$\frac{1}{6}$_____   6. $\frac{4}{5} \times 30$ _____24_____

7. $\frac{2}{6}$ of 60 _____20_____   8. $\frac{6}{5} \times \frac{3}{8}$ _____$\frac{9}{20}$_____

In which number does the digit 7 have the greater value?

9. a. 8709   b. 17,402   ___b___

10. a. 178,526   b. 281,708   ___a___

11. a. 1,927,415   b. 7,581,620   ___b___

12. a. 27,956,200 b. 61,749,032   ___a___

Solve.

13. The Young Talent Music School is having a recital by 4 students. In how many different orders can the students perform?

14. Mrs. Carnevale supplied the refreshments for the recital. She bought 2 gallons of apple cider at $3.50 per gallon and 4 dozen muffins at $2.25 per dozen. Did she spend more or less than $20?

____24____   ___less than $20___

Name _____

Accept any reasonable estimate.
Estimate the sum or difference.

1. $7\frac{1}{5} + 1\frac{2}{3}$ _____ 9

2. $6\frac{1}{4} - 2\frac{9}{10}$ _____ 3

3. $\frac{3}{4} + \frac{9}{16} + \frac{6}{7}$ _____ $2\frac{1}{2}$

4. $9\frac{4}{7} - 3\frac{5}{8}$ _____ 6

5. $8\frac{1}{3} - 3\frac{8}{9}$ _____ 4

6. $5\frac{5}{6} + 4\frac{1}{7}$ _____ 10

7. $12\frac{1}{6} - 4\frac{9}{10}$ _____ 7

8. $\frac{5}{12} + \frac{3}{4} + \frac{2}{5}$ _____ 2

Use cross products to solve each proportion.

9. $\frac{3}{5} = \frac{r}{25}$ _____ $r = 15$

10. $\frac{80}{s} = \frac{10}{9}$ _____ $s = 72$

11. $\frac{t}{15} = \frac{8}{10}$ _____ $t = 12$

12. $\frac{14}{12} = \frac{21}{v}$ _____ $v = 18$

13. $\frac{7}{k} = \frac{35}{40}$ _____ $k = 8$

14. $\frac{2}{3} = \frac{w}{15}$ _____ $w = 10$

Solve.

15. Sam made a scale model of a dog house he wants to build. The model is 4 inches tall. He used a scale of 1 in. = 1 ft. How tall will the actual dog house be?

_____ 4 feet _____

16. Cara is drawing a plan for her garden. Her garden area measures 24 feet by 12 feet. If she uses a scale of 1 in. = 2 ft, what will the dimensions be of her drawing?

_____ 12 inches by 6 inches _____

Name _____

Choose *a* or *b* and compute the answer.

1. a. $16 \times \frac{5}{8}$ _____ 10   **b.** 16×0.625 _____ 10

2. a. $18\frac{1}{8} \times \frac{1}{5}$ _____ $3\frac{5}{8}$ **b.** 18.125×0.2 _____ 3.625

3. a. $18\frac{2}{5} \div 2\frac{1}{10}$ _____ 4   **b.** $8.4 \div 2.1$ _____ 4

4. a. $35\frac{5}{8} \div 9\frac{1}{2}$ _____ $3\frac{3}{4}$ **b.** $35.625 \div 9.5$ _____ 3.75

5. a. $1\frac{3}{4} \times \frac{2}{5}$ _____ $\frac{7}{10}$ **b.** 1.75×0.4 _____ 0.7

6. a. $\frac{3}{4} \times \frac{1}{2}$ _____ $\frac{3}{8}$ **b.** 0.75×0.5 _____ 0.375

Solve.

7. $6q = 54$ _____ $q = 9$ **8.** $64 = 4a$ _____ $a = 16$

9. $9t = 450$ _____ $t = 50$ **10.** $160 = 20w$ _____ $w = 8$

11. $25y = 375$ _____ $y = 15$ **12.** $11p = 121$ _____ $p = 11$

Solve.

13. If you were to toss a penny 50 times, predict how many times you would get heads.

14. Luanne tossed a coin 300 times in an experiment. She got heads 177 times. How many more times did she get heads than you would predict?

_____ about 25 times _____

_____ 27 more times _____

136 DAILY CUMULATIVE REVIEW

Write the answer. Use mental math.

1. $7.30 + $1.95 _____$9.25_____

2. 76 − 29 _____47_____

3. 55 − 17 _____38_____

4. 220 + 180 _____400_____

5. 34 + 79 _____113_____

6. $11.00 − $6.99 _____$4.01_____

7. 528 + 298 _____826_____

8. 83 − 27 _____56_____

Classify each angle as *acute*, *right*, *obtuse*, or *straight*.

9. ∠ FBG

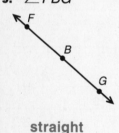

_____straight_____

10. ∠ MNS

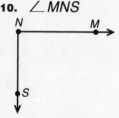

_____right_____

11. ∠ PQT

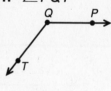

_____obtuse_____

Solve.

For one week, Tracey recorded these daily high temperatures: 75°, 82°, 79°, 71°, 68°, 76°, and 74°.

12. What was the mean of the temperatures? _____75°_____

13. What was the range of the temperatures? _____14°_____

Name _____

137 DAILY CUMULATIVE REVIEW

Estimate the quotient.

1. $7\overline{)314}$ 40–50

2. $42\overline{)7623}$ 100–200

3. $65\overline{)459}$ 6–7

4. $4\overline{)13,110}$ 3000–4000

5. $37\overline{)634}$ 10–20

6. $5\overline{)8020}$ 1000–2000

7. $580 \div 6$ _____ 90–100

8. $6890 \div 71$ _____ 90–100

Order each set of numbers from least to greatest.

9. $\frac{3}{8}, \frac{1}{6}, \frac{2}{5}$ _____ $\frac{1}{6}, \frac{3}{8}, \frac{2}{5}$

10. $\frac{2}{3}, \frac{9}{10}, \frac{11}{12}, \frac{3}{4}$ _____ $\frac{2}{3}, \frac{3}{4}, \frac{9}{10}, \frac{11}{12}$

11. $5\frac{2}{3}, 6\frac{1}{2}, 5\frac{5}{8}, 6\frac{7}{12}$ _____ $5\frac{5}{8}, 5\frac{2}{3}, 6\frac{1}{2}, 6\frac{7}{12}$

12. $9\frac{1}{6}, 9\frac{3}{8}, 7\frac{5}{16}, 8\frac{1}{2}$ _____ $7\frac{5}{16}, 8\frac{1}{2}, 9\frac{1}{6}, 9\frac{3}{8}$

Solve.

13. Meredith is playing a game using a number cube. The sides are numbered from 1 to 6. What is the probability that her next roll will result in a 5? _____ $\frac{1}{6}$

14. What is the probability that her next roll will result in a 7 or a greater number? _____ 0

DAILY CUMULATIVE REVIEW ·····················

Write the answer.

1.
```
   489
×   63
30,807
```

2.
```
     6
− 3.485
 2.515
```

3.
```
  839
  190
+ 249
 1278
```

4.
```
  0.75
8) 6
```

5.
```
     $2.61
11) $28.71
```

6.
```
     200
0.07) 14
```

7. 5385 + 7808 ___13,193___

8. 28 × $4.20 ___$117.60___

Tell whether the figure and its image show a slide or a flip.

9.

_____flip_____

10.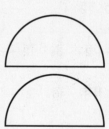

_____slide_____

11.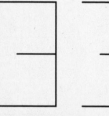

_____slide_____

12.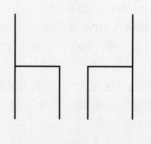

_____flip_____

Name _____

Write the answer.

1. $14\frac{2}{5}$
    $+ \ 5\frac{2}{5}$
    _____
    $19\frac{4}{5}$

2. 7
    $- 1\frac{5}{16}$
    _____
    $5\frac{11}{16}$

3. $16\frac{3}{10}$
    $- 12\frac{4}{5}$
    _____
    $3\frac{1}{2}$

4. $21\frac{4}{9}$
    $+ \ 3\frac{2}{9}$
    _____
    $24\frac{2}{3}$

5. $5\frac{3}{8}$
    $+ 4\frac{1}{2}$
    _____
    $9\frac{7}{8}$

6. 20
    $- \ 6\frac{7}{10}$
    _____
    $13\frac{3}{10}$

7. $7\frac{1}{2} \times 3\frac{1}{6}$ _____ $23\frac{3}{4}$

8. $18 \div \frac{3}{5}$ _____ 30

9. $\frac{1}{2} \times \frac{5}{6} \times \frac{4}{5}$ _____ $\frac{1}{3}$

10. $\frac{1}{2} + \frac{5}{6} + \frac{4}{5}$ _____ $2\frac{2}{15}$

Use the spinner to answer each question.

11. What is the probability of spinning 1?

    $\frac{2}{6}$ or $\frac{1}{3}$
    _____

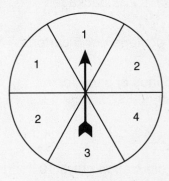

12. What is the probability of spinning 3?

    $\frac{1}{6}$
    _____

13. What is the probability of spinning 2 or 4?

    $\frac{3}{6}$ or $\frac{1}{2}$
    _____

14. What is the probability of spinning 5?

    0
    _____

Name _____

140 DAILY CUMULATIVE REVIEW

Write the answer. Use mental math.

1. $\frac{3}{4} + \frac{1}{4}$ _____ 1

2. $5\frac{1}{3} + 2\frac{1}{3}$ _____ $7\frac{2}{3}$

3. $10 - 3\frac{1}{2}$ _____ $6\frac{1}{2}$

4. $\frac{7}{8} - \frac{1}{8}$ _____ $\frac{6}{8}$ or $\frac{3}{4}$

5. $8\frac{2}{5} + 4\frac{3}{5}$ _____ 13

6. $3\frac{3}{4} + 2\frac{1}{2}$ _____ $6\frac{1}{4}$

7. $4 - \frac{2}{3}$ _____ $3\frac{1}{3}$

8. $6\frac{1}{2} - 3\frac{1}{2}$ _____ 3

Write each ratio three different ways.

9. 6 red tiles to 7 blue tiles _____ 6 to 7; 6:7; $\frac{6}{7}$

10. 10 books to 1 shelf _____ 10 to 1; 10:1; $\frac{10}{1}$

11. 3 miles in 45 minutes _____ 3 to 45; 3:45; $\frac{3}{45}$

12. 14 pens in 2 packages _____ 14 to 2; 14:2; $\frac{14}{2}$

13. $14 postage per 5 cartons _____ 14 to 5; 14:5; $\frac{14}{5}$

14. 7 pounds of sand for 4 fish tanks _____ 7 to 4; 7:4; $\frac{7}{4}$

Solve.

15. A radio station plays 10 songs every 45 minutes. How many songs are played in $1\frac{1}{2}$ hours? _____ 20 songs

16. At the rate of 10 songs every 45 minutes, how long would it take to play 50 songs? _____ 225 minutes or 3 h 45 min

Name _____

DAILY CUMULATIVE REVIEW

Estimate.

Accept all reasonable estimates.

1. $\frac{4}{5}$ of 91 ___about 80___

2. $\frac{1}{4}$ of \$63 ___about \$15–\$20___

3. $\frac{1}{3}$ of 190 ___about 60___

4. $\frac{2}{5}$ of 290 ___about 120___

5. $\frac{1}{7}$ of 414 ___about 50–60___

6. $\frac{1}{8}$ of 592 ___about 70–80___

7. $\frac{3}{4}$ of 812 ___about 600___

8. $\frac{2}{3}$ of \$406 ___about \$260–\$300___

Write the prime factorization of each number. If a number is already prime, write the word _prime_.

9. 60 ___ $2 \times 2 \times 3 \times 5$ ___

10. 32 ___ $2 \times 2 \times 2 \times 2 \times 2$ ___

11. 59 ___ prime ___

12. 140 ___ $2 \times 2 \times 5 \times 7$ ___

13. 108 ___ $2 \times 2 \times 3 \times 3 \times 3$ ___

14. 205 ___ 5×41 ___

Solve.

15. Mrs. Kwan is buying carpet for her living room, which measures 4 yards by 6 yards. The carpeting she wants costs \$21 a square yard. How much will it cost to buy carpet for the room? ___\$504___

Name _____

Write the answer.

1.
$$3.04$$
$$\times\ 1.5$$
$$\overline{4.56}$$

2.
$$5\frac{1}{3}$$
$$+\ 2\frac{1}{5}$$
$$\overline{7\frac{8}{15}}$$

3.
$$7\frac{1}{2}$$
$$-\ 4\frac{3}{4}$$
$$\overline{2\frac{3}{4}}$$

4.
$$136$$
$$\times\ 51$$
$$\overline{6936}$$

5.
$$0.09$$
$$\times\ 0.9$$
$$\overline{0.081}$$

6.
$$\overset{137\ R25}{72\overline{)9889}}$$

7. $\frac{5}{6} + \frac{5}{12} + \frac{1}{4}$ _____ $1\frac{1}{2}$

8. $25.80 ÷ 15 _____ $1.72

Write the letter of the proportion that matches the problem. Solve.

When Mrs. Acosta's class does an art project, each group of 3 students gets 8 markers, 2 pairs of scissors, and 1 roll of tape.

9. How many markers does she need for 12 students?

a; 32 markers

a. $\dfrac{3\ students}{8\ markers} = \dfrac{12\ students}{n\ markers}$

b. $\dfrac{3\ students}{8\ markers} = \dfrac{n\ markers}{12\ students}$

10. How many pairs of scissors does she need for 6 students?

b; 4 pairs of scissors

a. $\dfrac{3\ students}{2\ pairs\ of\ scissors} = \dfrac{n\ pairs\ of\ scissors}{6\ students}$

b. $\dfrac{3\ students}{2\ pairs\ of\ scissors} = \dfrac{6\ students}{n\ pairs\ of\ scissors}$

143 DAILY CUMULATIVE REVIEW

Write the answer.

1. $2.26
    6.07
    + 4.98
    ─────
    $13.31

2.   3
    − 0.647
    ───────
     2.353

3.   9.03
    ×   25
    ───────
    225.75

4. 0.05
    0.3)0.015

5.   18.713
    +   4.135
    ─────────
       22.848

6.   58.853
    − 27.677
    ─────────
       31.176

7. 16.5 × 100 ___1650___

8. 77 ÷ 1000 ___0.077___

9. 19.67 + 3.8 ___23.47___

10. 46 − 23.087 ___22.913___

Measure each scale drawing to the nearest unit. Then use a proportion to help you calculate the actual measurement.

11.

Study For Success

1 cm = 10 cm

___55 centimeters___

12.

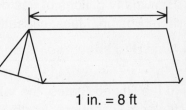

1 in. = 8 ft

___12 feet___

Name _____

144 DAILY CUMULATIVE REVIEW

Answers may vary. Accept any reasonable estimate.
Estimate the product.

1. 589 × 8 ___4000–4800___   **2.** 48 × 78 ___4000___

3. 5 × $2.57 ___$10–$15___   **4.** 32 × 615 ___18,000___

5. 6 × 976 ___6000___   **6.** 8 × $7.92 ___$64___

7. 79 × 86 ___6400–7200___   **8.** 61 × 290 ___18,000___

**Write each fraction or mixed number as an
equivalent decimal.**

9. $6\frac{3}{5}$ ___6.6___   **10.** $7\frac{3}{20}$ ___7.15___   **11.** $\frac{9}{5}$ ___1.8___

12. $\frac{49}{100}$ ___0.49___   **13.** $8\frac{15}{50}$ ___8.3___   **14.** $\frac{3}{12}$ ___0.25___

**Read the problem. If there is not enough
information, tell what you need to know, and, if
possible, find the information to solve the problem.**

15. Mr. Lee's car averages 27 miles per gallon of gas.
How many gallons of gas does he need to drive
from Boston, Massachusetts to Atlanta, Georgia?

___need to know the number of miles from Boston to___
___Atlanta (1037 miles); 38.4 gallons___

16. In the United States, the tallest structure is the TV
tower in Blanchard, North Dakota. At 2,063 feet, it
is 609 feet taller than the tallest building, the
Sears Tower in Chicago. How tall is the Sears
Tower?

___1454 feet___

Name _____

Write the answer.

1. $5\overline{)713}$ 142 R3

2. $\begin{array}{r} 6.71 \\ \times\ \ 2.8 \\ \hline 18.788 \end{array}$

3. $18\overline{)91.26}$ 5.07

4. $7\frac{1}{3} \times \frac{1}{8}$ _____ $\frac{11}{12}$

5. $1\frac{1}{8} \div \frac{1}{9}$ _____ $10\frac{1}{8}$

6. $\$75 \times \frac{1}{3}$ _____ $\$25$

7. $2.05 \div 0.1$ _____ 20.5

Complete. Write <, >, or = .

8. 7000 mL $\boxed{>}$ 6.2 L

9. 120 mm $\boxed{<}$ 12 m

10. 0.55 m $\boxed{=}$ 55 cm

11. 0.96 L $\boxed{=}$ 960 mL

12. 11,000 g $\boxed{>}$ 0.11 kg

13. 84 cm $\boxed{<}$ 8400 mm

Solve.

14. Mr. Echohawk bought $\frac{1}{4}$ pound of peanuts, $\frac{1}{4}$ pound of cashews, $\frac{1}{2}$ pound of raisins, and $\frac{1}{4}$ pound of sunflower seeds. Did he buy more or less than 2 pounds of snacks?

_____ less

15. Lena made a loaf of fruit bread. She took half of it to school to share with friends. She cut that part into 8 equal pieces. What fraction of the original loaf was each piece?

$\frac{1}{16}$ of the
_____
original loaf

Write the answer. Use mental math.

1. 80×70 _____5600_____

2. 50×300 _____15,000_____

3. 3.10×10 _____$31_____

4. 50×50 _____2500_____

5. 200×50 _____10,000_____

6. 2.8×100 _____280_____

7. $2 \times 25 \times 5$ _____250_____

8. 0.6×1000 _____600_____

Use the figures below to answer exercise 9.

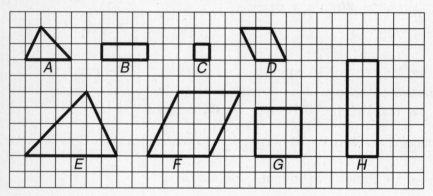

9. Tell which pairs of figures in the diagram are similar.

_____B, H; C, G_____

147 DAILY CUMULATIVE REVIEW

Divide. Round the quotient to the given place.

1. cent $5.03 ÷ 11 $0.46

2. hundredths   202.9 ÷ 6   33.82

3. tenths   1.9 ÷ 7   0.3

4. thousandths   4.722 ÷ 15   0.315

5. hundredths   70.97 ÷ 8   8.87

6. cent $35.39 ÷ 5 $7.08

7. thousandths   9)‾2   0.222

8. tenths   18.9 ÷ 6   3.2

Use the cross–products method to check whether the ratios are equal. Write *yes* or *no*.

9. $\frac{5}{7}, \frac{20}{35}$ **10.** $\frac{4}{6}, \frac{10}{15}$ **11.** $\frac{7}{10}, \frac{9}{12}$

no   yes   no

Solve.

12. Ms. Parks makes apple nut muffins using 1 cup of nuts for every 2 cups of flour. Her neighbor, Ms. Abbott, makes the same kind of muffins using 1 cup of nuts for every 3 cups of flour. Whose muffins are nuttier?

Ms. Parks

Name _____

Write the product. You may use a calculator.

1. 854
    × 607
    518,378

2. 921
    × 782
    720,222

3. 7212
    × 942
    6,793,704

4. 91,300
    × 700
    63,910,000

5. 59,000
    × 2,800
    165,200,000

6. 12,000,000
    × 431
    5,172,000,000

Write the missing angle measure for each quadrilateral.

7. Quadrilateral *RSTU*

   $\angle R = 90°$; $\angle S = 90°$; $\angle T = 130°$; $\angle U = $ __50°__

8. Quadrilateral *MNPQ*

   $\angle M = 120°$; $\angle N = 35°$; $\angle P = $ __55°__ ; $\angle Q = 150°$

Draw all the lines of symmetry for each figure.

9.
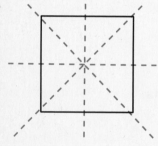

10.

149 ◣ DAILY CUMULATIVE REVIEW
··

Solve. Use mental math.

1. 25% of 400 ____100____   2. 10% of 80 ____8____

3. 50% of 70 ____35____   4. 25% of 200 ____50____

5. 50% of 300 ____150____   6. 10% of 110 ____11____

7. 20% of 50 ____10____   8. 50% of 24 ____12____

9. 25% of 60 ____15____   10. 20% of 250 ____50____

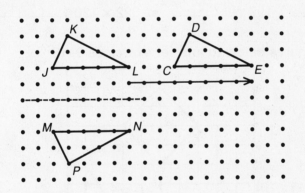

For the slide shown, complete each statement.

11. $\overline{JL} \cong$ ____$\overline{CE}$____   12. $\overline{KJ} \parallel$ ____$\overline{DC}$____   13. $\angle L \cong$ ____$\angle E$____

For the flip shown, complete each statement.

14. $\overline{KL} \cong$ ____$\overline{PN}$____   15. $\angle K \cong$ ____$\angle P$____   16. $\angle J \cong$ ____$\angle M$____

150 DAILY CUMULATIVE REVIEW

Write the answer.

1.
```
   308
   889
 + 485
 ─────
  1682
```

2.
```
   5500
 - 1162
 ──────
   4338
```

3.
```
    403
 ×    5
 ──────
   2015
```

4.
```
      4 R31
 53) 243
```

5.
```
   7082
 - 4940
 ──────
   2142
```

6.
```
      4341 R5
 7) 30392
```

7. 963 + 22 + 197 __1182__   8. 622 × 120 ___74,640___

Use the figures below to answer exercises 9–13.

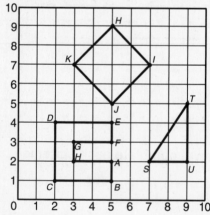

9. Which figures have line symmetry?   *HIJK,*
   ABCDEFGH

10. Which figures have turn symmetry?   ___HIJK___

Write the ordered pair for each point.

11. *K* __(3,7)__   12. *F* __(5,3)__   13. *S* __(7,2)__

Name _____

151 DAILY CUMULATIVE REVIEW

Estimate.   Answers may vary. Possible answers are shown.

1. 27% of 40 _____10_____   **2.** 9% of 20 _____2_____

3. 48% of 80 _____40_____   **4.** 53% of 40 _____20_____

5. 23% of 160 _____40_____   **6.** 19% of 20 _____4_____

7. 51% of 200 _____100_____   **8.** 11% of 50 _____5_____

Use the data to complete exercises 9–11.

During the semester, members of the Reading
Club recorded the number of books each member
read. The club wants to make a line-plot to
display the data. Here are the numbers of books
read by the different club members:
6, 10,12, 10, 13, 7, 6, 9, 9, 14, 10, 15, 10, 12, 15.

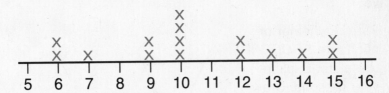

9. Complete the line-plot.

10. How many students read 9 or 10
books?   6 students

11. How many students read 12 or more
books?   6 students

Name _____

Write the answer.

1. $819.54
    405.66
    + 291.01
    _____
    $1516.21

2. 44.033
    - 9.2
    _____
    34.833

3. 85,669
    - 17,015
    _____
    68,654

4. $\frac{3}{4} + \frac{7}{16} + \frac{5}{8}$ ____ $1\frac{13}{16}$ ____

5. $19\frac{5}{8} - 3\frac{1}{4}$ ____ $16\frac{3}{8}$ ____

6. $864 + 707$ ____ 1571 ____

7. $4\frac{9}{10} + 2\frac{2}{5} + \frac{1}{10}$ ____ $7\frac{2}{5}$ ____

Write as a percent.

8. $\frac{3}{5}$ ____ 60% ____

9. 0.65 ____ 65% ____

10. 3.25 ____ 325% ____

11. 0.8 ____ 80% ____

12. $\frac{19}{50}$ ____ 38% ____

13. $\frac{9}{100}$ ____ 9% ____

Solve.

14. Predict whether or not figure *ABCD* will tesselate. Explain your reasons. Draw a picture.

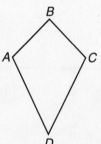

_____ Yes; explanations may vary. _____

_____

_____

DAILY CUMULATIVE REVIEW

Estimate.   Answers may vary. Accept any reasonable estimate.

1. 6747 − 1012 ___6000___

2. 8456 + 5987 ___14,000–14,500___

3. 57 × 699 ___42,000___

4. 2621 ÷ 3 ___800–900___

5. 2851 − 634 ___2000___

6. 148 + 74 + 440 ___600–700___

7. 89 × 62 ___5400–6000___

8. 5670 ÷ 21 ___300___

Find the item with the lowest unit price in each group. Write a, b, or c. You may be able to find it by estimating.

9. a. 1 T-shirt for $4.00   ___c___
   b. 3 T-shirts for $9.00
   c. 5 T-shirts for $12.50

10. a. 4-oz bag of peanuts for $0.89   ___b___
   b. 8-oz bag of peanuts for $1.59
   c. 16-oz bag of peanuts for $3.56

11. a. 2 tapes for $4.25   ___a___
   b. 5 tapes for $11.25
   c. 10 tapes for $22.00

12. a. 3-pack of juice for $1.19   ___c___
   b. 6-pack of juice for $2.45
   c. 24-pack of juice for $8.72

Name _____

154 DAILY CUMULATIVE REVIEW

Write the answer.

1. $9\frac{3}{8}$
    $+ 2\frac{1}{3}$
    $\overline{11\frac{17}{24}}$

2. $\begin{array}{r} 1.35 \\ \times\ \ 0.4 \\ \hline 0.54 \end{array}$

3. $3\frac{3}{4}$
    $- 1\frac{1}{4}$
    $\overline{2\frac{1}{2}}$

4. $6\overline{)\$21.48}^{\$3.58}$

5. $27\overline{)9258}^{342\ R24}$

6. $\begin{array}{r} 3.107 \\ +\ 1.0411 \\ \hline 4.1481 \end{array}$

7. $\frac{1}{2} + \frac{1}{6} + \frac{1}{3}$ ___ 1

8. $6\frac{1}{6} \times 9$ ___ $55\frac{1}{2}$

9. $75.3 \div 6$ ___ 12.55

10. $20 - 3.087$ ___ 16.913

Use the figures below to answer questions 11–14.

  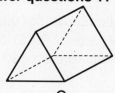 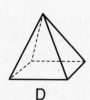

A   B   C   D

11. Which figures are prisms? ___ B, C

12. Which figures are polyhedrons? ___ B, C, D

13. Which figures have at least one face
    that is a triangle? ___ C, D

14. Which figures have at least one face
    that is a rectangle? ___ B, C, D

Name _____

....

Write the answer. Use mental math.

1. $\frac{1}{2} + \frac{1}{4}$ _____ $\frac{3}{4}$

2. $\frac{2}{5} + \frac{3}{5}$ _____ 1

3. $1 - \frac{1}{6}$ _____ $\frac{5}{6}$

4. $2\frac{1}{2} + \frac{3}{4}$ _____ $3\frac{1}{4}$

5. $3\frac{1}{4} + 2\frac{1}{2}$ _____ $5\frac{3}{4}$

6. $3 - \frac{2}{3}$ _____ $2\frac{1}{3}$

7. $10 - \frac{5}{12}$ _____ $9\frac{7}{12}$

8. $3\frac{3}{8} + 3\frac{3}{8}$ _____ $6\frac{6}{8}$ or $6\frac{3}{4}$

Compute. Look for ways to use mental math.

9. 8% of 69 _____ 5.52

10. 15% of 300 _____ 45

11. 10% of 67 _____ 6.7

12. 45% of 120 _____ 54

13. 84% of 100 _____ 84

14. 25% of 200 _____ 50

15. 32% of 50 _____ 16

16. 75% of 120 _____ 90

Solve.

17. During a local election, a survey of 150 people showed that 36% favor the current mayor. How many of the people in the survey favor the current mayor?

_____ 54 people

18. Of the 150 people surveyed, 12 said they intended to write in a candidate. What percent of the total number of people surveyed is that?

_____ 8%

Name _____

 DAILY CUMULATIVE REVIEW ....

Find the total cost of each item. You may use a calculator.

1. $13.50 sweater; 4% tax $14.04

2. $1.50 card of buttons; 6% tax $1.59

3. $4.80 picture album; 5% tax $5.04

4. $185.00 camera; 3% tax $190.55

5. $10.00 calculator; 7% tax $10.70

6. $29.50 backpack; 4% tax $30.68

7. $500 sofa, now 15% off; 5% sales tax $446.25

Figure *GFED* is the quarter–turn image of figure *ABCD*.

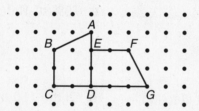

8. Which line segment in figure *GFED* is
   congruent to $\overline{CD}$? $\overline{ED}$

9. Which angle in figure *GFED* is
   congruent to ∠*ABC*?   ∠*GFE*

10. What kind of angle is ∠*ADC*?   **right angle,
                                                     or 90°**

157 DAILY CUMULATIVE REVIEW

Write the answer. Use mental math.

1. $\frac{1}{4}$ of 44 _____11_____

2. $\frac{3}{8}$ of 32 _____12_____

3. $\frac{2}{5}$ of 40 _____16_____

4. $\frac{1}{8}$ of 56 _____7_____

5. $\frac{1}{10}$ of 240 _____24_____

6. $\frac{1}{6}$ of 420 _____70_____

7. $\frac{1}{3}$ of 300 _____100_____

8. $\frac{3}{10}$ of 90 _____27_____

Write a fraction and a percent for each area.

9. shaded with

   $\frac{2}{5}$ or $\frac{40}{100}$; 40%

10. shaded with

    $\frac{9}{25}$ or $\frac{36}{100}$; 36%

11. not shaded

    $\frac{6}{25}$ or $\frac{24}{100}$; 24%

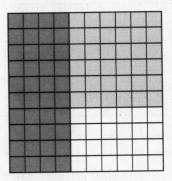

The price of each item below is reduced by 15%. Write the discount and the sale price for each. You may use a calculator.

12. a $47.00 ladder _____$7.05; $39.95_____

13. a $12.60 shovel _____$1.89; $10.71_____

14. a $3.98 flashlight _____$0.60; $3.38_____

15. a $22.50 grill _____$3.38; $19.12_____

Use the chart to complete exercises 1–3.

1. What is the total budget for the overnight camping trip?

$400

2. Complete the chart.

Hiking Club Budget

Item	Cost	Fraction of Total Cost	Percent of Total Cost	Number of Degrees
Food	$200	$\frac{200}{400}$	50%	180°
Campground Fee	$60	$\frac{60}{400}$	15%	54°
Travel	$80	$\frac{80}{400}$	20%	72°
Tent Rent	$40	$\frac{40}{400}$	10%	36°
First Aid Kits	$20	$\frac{20}{400}$	5%	18°

3. Use a protractor and a ruler to draw the missing sections of the circle graph.

Hiking Club Camping Budget

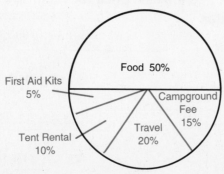

Name _____

••

Estimate.   Answers may vary. Accept any reasonable estimate.

1. $9.2 + 0.9 + 6.14$ ___16___   **2.** $28.3 - 5.84$ ___20–22___

3. $7 \times \$3.19$ ___\$21___   **4.** $\$34.85 \div 6$ ___\$5–\$6___

5. $44.1 + 15 + 5.7$ ___60–65___   **6.** $16.59 - 0.21$ ___16___

7. $9 \times \$2.61$ ___\$18–\$27___   **8.** $\$146.78 \div 8$ ___\$10–\$20___

Write each probability in the form of a ratio.

9. What is the probability of picking a card with a star?

$\frac{3}{9}$ or $\frac{1}{3}$

10. What is the probability of picking a card with either a circle or a diamond?

$\frac{6}{9}$ or $\frac{2}{3}$

11. What is the probability of picking a card with a square?

$\frac{0}{9}$ or 0

12. What is the probability of picking a card with a shape on it?

$\frac{9}{9}$ or 1

Name _____

Write the answer.

1.
$$515 \times 77 = 39{,}655$$

2. $0.3 \overline{)9.3}$ → 31

3. $4 \overline{)11}$ → 2.75

4.
$$3.91 \times 48 = 187.68$$

5.
$$0.71$$
$$8.9$$
$$+ 5.61$$
$$15.22$$

6.
$$23$$
$$- 8.92$$
$$14.08$$

7. $9 \times \$2.40$ ___$21.60___

8. $9.55 \div 100$ ___0.0955___

Use cross products to solve each proportion.

9. $\frac{2}{8} = \frac{h}{36}$ ___$h = 9$___

10. $\frac{24}{m} = \frac{8}{18}$ ___$m = 54$___

11. $\frac{c}{27} = \frac{7}{9}$ ___$c = 21$___

12. $\frac{4}{w} = \frac{16}{40}$ ___$w = 10$___

Solve each problem. Write an equation or use other strategies. **Equations may vary.**

13. Tickets for the PTA picnic cost $3 each. The food budget is $150 and the decoration budget is $15. How many tickets must be sold to pay for the food and the decorations?

$\frac{\$165}{\$3} = t$; **55 tickets**

14. A pony ride lasts 5 minutes, and 6 children can ride the ponies at one time. How long will it take for 48 children to ride the ponies?

$\frac{6}{5} = \frac{48}{m}$; **40 minutes**

Name _____

Write the answer. Use mental math.

1. 51.1 × 10 ___511___

2. 0.53 × 100 ___53___

3. 94 ÷ 10 ___9.4___

4. 2.9 ÷ 100 ___0.029___

5. 45 × 1000 ___45,000___

6. 0.036 × 100 ___3.6___

7. 5 ÷ 1000 ___0.005___

8. 1.95 ÷ 10 ___0.195___

9. 4.7 ÷ 100 ___0.047___

10. 10.22 × 10 ___102.2___

11. 850 ÷ 1000 ___0.85___

12. 13.609 × 1000 ___13,609___

Find the area of each geoboard figure below.

13.

___6 units²___

14.
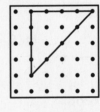
___8 units²___

15.
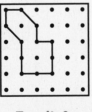
___7 units²___

16.
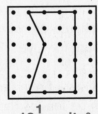
___$12\frac{1}{2}$ units²___

Name _____

 DAILY CUMULATIVE REVIEW

Write the product or the quotient. Use mental math when you can.

1. 315 ÷ 3 _____105_____   **2.** 208 ÷ 4 _____52_____

3. 41 × 7 _____287_____   **4.** 31 × 5 _____155_____

5. $60\overline{)12,000}$ with 200 above   **6.** $90\overline{)3600}$ with 40 above   **7.** $40\overline{)800}$ with 20 above

Write as a percent.

8. $\frac{73}{100}$ ___73%___   **9.** 0.64 ___64%___   **10.** 2.55 ___255%___

11. $\frac{14}{10}$ ___140%___   **12.** 0.87 ___87%___   **13.** $\frac{1}{25}$ ___4%___

14. $\frac{3}{20}$ ___15%___   **15.** 1.25 ___125%___   **16.** $\frac{4}{5}$ ___80%___

Solve.

Dean put $200 in a savings account that pays an interest rate of 6% per year.

17. How much interest will he receive on that amount for 1 year?   ___$12___

18. How much will be in the account after 2 years if he leaves the interest in the account?   ___$224.72___

163 DAILY CUMULATIVE REVIEW

Write the answer.

1. $9\frac{7}{10}$
   $+ 3\frac{2}{15}$
   _____
   $12\frac{5}{6}$

2. $10\frac{5}{9}$
   $- 6\frac{1}{9}$
   _____
   $4\frac{4}{9}$

3. $8\frac{2}{3}$
   $+ 3\frac{1}{5}$
   _____
   $11\frac{13}{15}$

4. $\frac{3}{8} \times 10$ _____ $3\frac{3}{4}$

5. $8\frac{1}{2} \div 2\frac{1}{2}$ _____ $3\frac{2}{5}$

6. $4\frac{1}{6} \div 1\frac{2}{3}$ _____ $2\frac{1}{2}$

7. $21 \times \frac{2}{3}$ _____ 14

Find the area and perimeter of each triangle.

8.

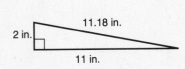

Area = _____ **11 in.²**

Perimeter = _____ **24.18 in.**

9.

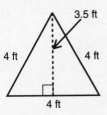

Area = _____ **7 ft²**

Perimeter = _____ **12 ft**

10.

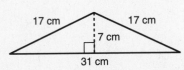

Area = _____ **A = 108.5 cm²**

Perimeter = _____ **65 cm**

11.

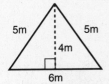

Area = _____ **12 m²**

Perimeter = _____ **16 m**

Name _____

Write the answer.

1. $36\overline{)483.84}$ **13.44**

2. $\begin{array}{r} \$2.87 \\ \times\quad 16 \\ \hline \$45.92 \end{array}$

3. $4\overline{)20.04}$ **5.01**

4. $\begin{array}{r} 8\frac{5}{6} \\ + 8\frac{5}{6} \\ \hline 17\frac{2}{3} \end{array}$

5. $\begin{array}{r} 2\frac{19}{100} \\ - 1\frac{1}{10} \\ \hline 1\frac{9}{100} \end{array}$

6. $\begin{array}{r} 7\frac{1}{2} \\ - 4\frac{1}{5} \\ \hline 3\frac{3}{10} \end{array}$

7. $1\frac{1}{8} \times 1\frac{5}{6}$ ___ $2\frac{1}{16}$

8. 1.25×0.5 ___ **0.625**

Write <, >, or = .

9. $\frac{2}{3}$ ⊙> $\frac{5}{8}$

10. $\frac{4}{7}$ ⊙> $\frac{1}{2}$

11. $\frac{1}{4}$ ⊙< $\frac{7}{15}$

12. $\frac{7}{10}$ ⊙> $\frac{7}{12}$

13. $8\frac{10}{30}$ ⊙= $8\frac{8}{24}$

14. $3\frac{1}{6}$ ⊙< $4\frac{2}{9}$

Solve.

15. In 1988, a family with an income of $25,000 living in Charlotte, North Carolina, paid 9% of their income for state and local taxes. How much money did they pay for these taxes? ___ **$2250**

165 DAILY CUMULATIVE REVIEW

Write the answer.

1. $\begin{array}{r} 601 \\ 3\overline{)1803} \end{array}$

2. $\begin{array}{r} 7700 \\ \times\ \ 68 \\ \hline 523{,}600 \end{array}$

3. $\begin{array}{r} 91 \\ \times 36 \\ \hline 3276 \end{array}$

3. $\begin{array}{r} 29{,}410 \\ +\ 17{,}221 \\ \hline 46{,}631 \end{array}$

5. $\begin{array}{r} \$83.98 \\ -\ \ 31.01 \\ \hline \$52.97 \end{array}$

6. $\begin{array}{r} 80{,}875 \\ -\ 9{,}478 \\ \hline 71{,}397 \end{array}$

7. 95 + 15 + 74 ___184___

8. 902 ÷ 3 ___300 R2___

Estimate the area of each drawing.

Accept any reasonable estimate.

9.
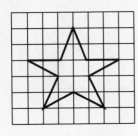

10.
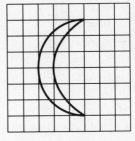

___10–11 units²___

___5–6 units²___

Solve.

11. Mrs. Cook has a circular table with a
diameter of 4 feet. She wants a table-
cloth that will hang 6 inches below the
edge of the table. To the nearest tenth
of a square foot, how much fabric will
be in the table cloth?

___19.6 ft²___

166 DAILY CUMULATIVE REVIEW

Add or subtract. You may use the table of measures in the Data Book section of your math book.

1.		2.		3.	
30 yd 5 in.		6 gal		2 yd 9 in.	
− 7 yd 3 in.		− 1 gal 3 qt		− 2 ft 3 in.	
23 yd 2 in.		4 gal 1 qt		1 yd 1 ft 6 in.	

4.		5.		6.	
9 ft 5 in.		8 lb 9 oz		3 h 33 min 6 s	
+ 8 ft 7 in.		+ 2 lb 13 oz		+ 1 h 18 min 55 s	
18 ft		11 lb 6 oz		4 h 52 min 1 s	

Draw dashed lines to show the hidden edges of each figure.

7.
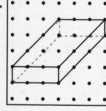

8.
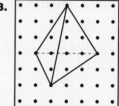

Sketch a cross section of each solid.

There are many possible cross sections.

9.
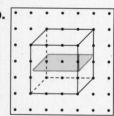

10.
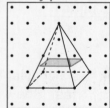

Name _____

Write the answer. Look for ways to use mental math.

1.
$$3\overline{)27.75} = 9.25$$

2.
$$12\overline{)10.32} = 0.86$$

3.
```
  5.05
  4.95
+ 6.66
 16.66
```

4.
```
  7.35
×   18
 132.3
```

5.
```
  4.3
× 0.4
 1.72
```

6.
```
  13
-  6 3/5
   6 2/5
```

7. $2.5 + 7.5 + 7.6$ __17.6__

8. $\$62.51 - \$1.99$ __\$60.52__

Find the area of each figure. Use 3.14 for π.

9.

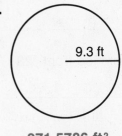

9.3 ft

__271.5786 ft²__

10.

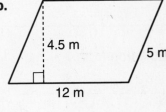

4.5 m

5 m

12 m

__54 m²__

11.

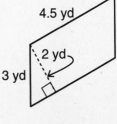

4.5 yd

2 yd

3 yd

__9 yd²__

12.

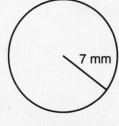

7 mm

__153.86 mm²__

Name _____

168 DAILY CUMULATIVE REVIEW

Estimate the sum or difference. Accept reasonable estimates.

1. $\frac{3}{10} + \frac{5}{6} + \frac{3}{8}$ _____2_____

2. $\frac{14}{15} - \frac{1}{4}$ _____$\frac{1}{2} - 1$_____

3. $\frac{2}{7} + \frac{9}{16}$ _____1_____

4. $7\frac{1}{2} - 1\frac{1}{8}$ _____$6\frac{1}{2}$_____

5. $\frac{3}{5} + \frac{8}{9} + \frac{5}{12}$ _____2_____

6. $9\frac{5}{6} - 4\frac{9}{10}$ _____5_____

7. $5\frac{7}{8} - 1\frac{4}{15}$ _____$4\frac{1}{2}$_____

8. $4\frac{1}{3} + \frac{2}{7} + 1\frac{3}{8}$ _____$6\frac{1}{2}$_____

Write the new temperature.

9. a 13° drop from 70°F

_____57°F_____

10. a 9° increase from ⁻3°C

_____6°C_____

11. a 17° drop from 15°C

_____⁻2°C_____

12. a 7° increase from ⁻15°F

_____⁻8°F_____

13. a 20° drop from 7°F

_____⁻13°F_____

14. a 42° increase from ⁻23°C

_____19°C_____

Solve.

A swimming pool is 20 feet long, 12 feet wide, and 5 feet deep.

15. How many cubic feet of water can the pool hold?

_____1200 ft³_____

16. If water flows into the pool at a rate of 2 cubic feet per minute, how many hours does it take to fill the pool?

_____10 hours_____

169 DAILY CUMULATIVE REVIEW

Answers may vary. Sample answers are given.

Estimate the quotient.

$0.40–$0.50
1. $7) \overline{\$2.95}$

$2.00–$3.00
2. $6) \overline{\$17.43}$

$0.60–$0.70
3. $4) \overline{\$2.71}$

$8.00–$9.00
4. $9) \overline{\$74.14}$

$200–$300
5. $3) \overline{\$642.72}$

$2.00–$3.00
6. $5) \overline{\$13.96}$

7. $\$51.76 \div 8$ __$6.00–$7.00__

8. $\$5.14 \div 3$ __$1.00–$2.00__

Find the area and perimeter of each figure.

9.

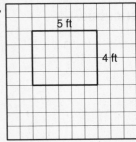

Area = ___20 ft²___

Perimeter = ___18 ft___

10.

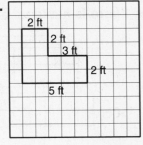

Area = ___14 ft²___

Perimeter = ___18 ft___

11.

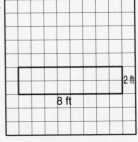

Area = ___16 ft²___

Perimeter = ___20 ft___

12.

Area = ___14 ft²___

Perimeter = ___16 ft___

DAILY CUMULATIVE REVIEW

Compute. Look for ways to use mental math.

1. 40% of 35 ___14___

2. 16% of 50 ___8___

3. 1% of 49 ___0.49___

4. 72% of 400 ___288___

5. 23% of 200 ___46___

6. 80% of 150 ___120___

7. 25% of 60 ___15___

8. 20% of 540 ___108___

This solid figure is made up of centimeter cubes.

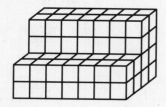

9. Find the volume and surface area of the figure.

_____ **volume = 84 cm³; surface area = 136 cm²** _____

Write an integer to describe each situation.

10. The lowest elevation in the Sahara is
440 feet below sea level.   ___⁻440 feet___

11. The highest elevation in Oregon is
Mount Hood, with an altitude of
11,239 feet above sea level.   ___⁺11,239 feet___

171 DAILY CUMULATIVE REVIEW

Write the answer.

1.
```
   1.42
   6.5
+ 2.05
─────
   9.97
```

2.
```
  33.009
−  8.1769
────────
  24.8321
```

3.
```
    7.52
×     19
──────
  142.88
```

4.
```
      $1.54
7)$10.78
```

5.
$$7\frac{3}{8}$$
$$+ 2\frac{1}{6}$$
$$\overline{9\frac{13}{24}}$$

6.
$$12\frac{2}{3}$$
$$- 4\frac{1}{5}$$
$$\overline{8\frac{7}{15}}$$

7. $9\frac{1}{2} \times 3\frac{3}{10}$ ___ $31\frac{7}{20}$ ___

8. $6 \div \frac{7}{10}$ ___ $8\frac{4}{7}$ ___

Find the volume. You may use a calculator.

9.

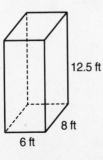

1½ in.
4 in.
6 in.

36 in.³

10.

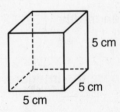

5 cm
5 cm
5 cm

125 cm³

11.

12.5 ft
8 ft
6 ft

600 ft³

12.

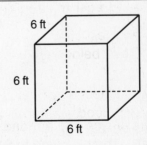

6 ft
6 ft
6 ft

216 ft³

172 DAILY CUMULATIVE REVIEW

Divide. Round the quotient to the given place.

1. cent $7.05 ÷ 8 $0.88

2. tenths   2.19 ÷ 18   0.1

3. hundredths   6.39 ÷ 7   0.91

4. thousandths 1.59 ÷ 16   0.099

5. tenths   775.4 ÷ 54   14.4

6. cent $45.80 ÷ 17 $2.69

7. thousandths 11 ÷ 12   0.917

8. hundredths   57.1 ÷ 4   14.28

Compare the integers. Write < or >.

9. ⁻6 $<$ ⁺5   **10.** 0 $<$ ⁺8   **11.** ⁻15 $<$ ⁺13

12. ⁺17 $>$ ⁻5   **13.** ⁻8 $>$ ⁻9   **14.** ⁻6 $<$ ⁻4

15. ⁻5 $<$ 0   **16.** ⁺3 $>$ ⁻6   **17.** ⁻10 $>$ ⁻100

Solve.

18. Mrs. Joyce and a friend had lunch at a cafe. The bill came to $12.50. The tip they left was 16% of the bill. How much money did they leave as a tip? $2.00

Name _____

173 DAILY CUMULATIVE REVIEW

Use counters to find the sum.

1. $^-5 + ^-1$ _____ $^-6$

2. $^-9 + ^+5$ _____ $^-4$

3. $^+7 + ^-6$ _____ $^+1$

4. $^+2 + ^+4$ _____ $^+6$

5. $^-9 + ^+2$ _____ $^-7$

6. $^-8 + ^-6$ _____ $^-14$

7. $^+6 + ^-7$ _____ $^-1$

8. $^-3 + ^+8$ _____ $^+5$

Use the grid to answer exercises 9–10.

9. Write the letter naming each of these points.

   a. (3, 1) _____ F

   b. (9, 2) _____ E

   c. (7, 8) _____ I

   d. (5, 6) _____ C

10. Write the ordered pair naming each of these points.

   a. A _____ (1,2)

   b. H _____ (4,4)

   c. J _____ (8,7)

   d. B _____ (2,7)

174 DAILY CUMULATIVE REVIEW

Add or subtract. Use counters to help.

1. +6 + −2 _____ +4 _____   2. +4 − +8 _____ −4 _____

3. +6 − +9 _____ −3 _____   4. −7 + +5 _____ −2 _____

5. −1 + +8 _____ +7 _____   6. +9 − +6 _____ +3 _____

7.   +3
  − +8
   −5

8.   −5
  + +5
    0

9.   +3
  − +4
   −1

Compute the interest made or paid in a year.

10. Buy a Computer
borrow: $2500
rate: 12%
_____ $300 _____

11. Vacation Fund
save: $800
rate: 6%
_____ $48 _____

12. Remodel a Kitchen
borrow: $10,000
rate: 9%
_____ $900 _____

13. Save for a House
save: $5000
rate: 7%
_____ $350 _____

Solve.

14. Martin's soccer team played
20 games. They tied 2 games, lost
6 games, and won all the rest. What
percent of the games did they win?
_____ 60% _____